The Natural Sciences
and The Christian Message

Other Books by the Author

Noise, 1954

Solid State Physical Electronics, 1957

Fluctuation Phenomena in Semiconductors, 1959

THE LUTHERAN STUDIES SERIES
Volume One

THE NATURAL SCIENCES AND THE CHRISTIAN MESSAGE

BY ALDERT VAN DER ZIEL, PH.D.
Professor of Electrical Engineering
The University of Minnesota

Publishers
T. S. DENISON & CO., INC.
Minneapolis

Copyright ©, 1960, by
LUTHERAN STUDIES, INC.

215
V242n

25400

Printed in the U. S. A.

By THE BRINGS PRESS

International Copyright Secured

Library of Congress Catalog Card Number: 60-9802

Introduction

This volume is one of a series called *Lutheran Studies*. This series, and each volume within it, seeks to give a hearing to scholars within the Christian Church, and the Lutheran Church in particular, who have found that their learning and research somehow relates to the life and beliefs of Christian people.

It is widely alleged in the twentieth century that detailed scholarship in many fields has rendered Christian theological views impossible and even false. Certain theologians have sometimes spoken categorically too, suggesting that these conflicts in loyalty and belief are clearly matters of sin and unbelief. However these matters ultimately will stand, this series of books is born of the conviction that the real or apparent conflicts between learning and faith must be resolved through detailed scholarship and considered judgment and by persons whose training and experience are sufficient to permit them to weigh the evidence, to assess the argument, and to draw conclusions in a responsible and measured manner.

A book like this one and those to follow are, after all, characteristic expressions of the Christian faith and of Lutheranism. The Protestant Reformation came in large part out of the work and experiences of university professors at Wittenberg, who courageously faced the intellectual and spiritual problems of their day and worked together to make their witness known. The Christian Church has similar resources today in the witness and integrity of its scholars, many of whom are, by virtue of their vocation and place of employment, outside of the orbit of religious orders and institutions. *Lutheran Studies* hopes to encourage these men and women to declare their needs, and to speak their minds to the end that the Christian message will ever be kept clear and the body of Christian believers strengthened. It is probably true that the scholars who speak out of the matrix of learning that appears secular, need the ear and fellowship of other believers and Lutheranism sometimes needs this kind of voice to stir its sluggish consciousness again.

This series was created initially by the action, in 1957, of the two campus pastors of the Lutheran Church (Missouri Synod) and the National Lutheran Council who were then at the University of Minnesota. They arranged for lectures to be delivered to interested parish pastors of the Twin City area by Lutheran professors whose teaching and research were in areas relevant to Christian faith, practice, and doctrine. As the lectures progressed, a concern grew up that these findings, which seemed timely, vital, and even necessary to the pastors, might be made available in a more permanent form for pastors and lay people, students and teachers, and in a larger geographical area. Further discussion led to the incorporation of *Lutheran Studies* as a nonprofit corporation. The incentive subsidy given by the Lutheran Brotherhood Life Insurance Company of Minneapolis not only makes this series initially possible, but also declares again their intention to promulgate activities commensurate with scholarship and the aims of Christian teaching.

It is hoped that two or three volumes of *Lutheran Studies* will be published each year. In accord with the purposes declared in its articles of incorporation, *Lutheran Studies* seeks to publish and to distribute volumes which will promote and encourage knowledge of the Lutheran faith, stimulate theological scholarship, and feed those kinds of educational and scientific concerns essential to theology and Christian practice. Accordingly volumes are projected on physical science, on contemporary philosophy, on the urban church and the sociology of the city, on some contemporary theologians, on the relationships between recent developmental psychology and the problem of Christian education, and other topics.

These are volumes of inquiry. They do not represent final positions upon the difficult matters which they assess. They are presented in the interest of "clarification" of the issues, of furthering discussion and study, albeit with the hope that the faith which overcomes the world might thereby abound.

REV. REUBEN C. BEISEL
President, St. John's College
Winfield, Kansas

LAWRENCE M. BRINGS
President, Minnesota
Protestant Foundation
Treasurer, *Lutheran Studies*

DR. ARMIN GRAMS
*Professor of Child
Development and Welfare*
University of Minnesota

DR. GEORGE F. HALL
*Campus Pastor for National
Lutheran Council students*
University of Minnesota
President, *Lutheran Studies*

DR. PAUL L. HOLMER
*Professor of Historical
Theology*
Divinity School
Yale University
New Haven, Connecticut

REV. HARRY N. HUXHOLD
Campus Pastor
The Lutheran Church
(Missouri Synod)
University of Minnesota

DR. ARTHUR L. JOHNSON
Professor of Sociology
University of Minnesota
Secretary, *Lutheran Studies*

DR. ROBERT F. SPENCER
Professor of Anthropology
University of Minnesota

DR. ALDERT VAN DER ZIEL
*Professor of Electrical
Engineering*
University of Minnesota
Vice President,
Lutheran Studies

Preface

This book is the result of a series of lectures on the natural sciences given for Lutheran pastors in the Lutheran Student Hall of the St. Paul Campus of the University of Minnesota.

The book is an attempt to demonstrate that the natural sciences and the Christian message are neither in harmony with each other, nor in conflict, but are radically different. It will be shown what the natural sciences are and aim at, and what the Christian message is and aims at. The real difference will then become apparent.

The book is based upon the premise that no adequate discussion about the relation between the natural sciences and the Christian message can be given unless sufficient time is spent to demonstrate what the natural sciences are and aim at. For that reason the largest part of the book is devoted to a discussion of the content and the procedures of the natural sciences, particularly physics and its borderline fields. If this had not been done, most of the statements made would have been without sufficient foundation. It is not necessary that this discussion be understood by every reader up to its last detail. It is sufficient if it is understood how the discussion leads to the conclusions made.

The book also deals with the certainty of our knowledge, with the meaning of the scientific procedures followed and with the relevance of the results obtained. Problems of this nature are usually discussed in textbooks on the philosophy of science. The present discussion deals mainly with those aspects of the problems that are important in physics instead of with those aspects that are chiefly of philosophical interest. A discussion of the latter aspects is not unimportant, but the author is of the opinion that it becomes more relevant after the first problem has been dealt with. Its development is left to the philosophers.

Some of the more outspoken statements made by the author are in disagreement with statements made by some prominent physicists. These disagreements do not involve the basic side of physics as such, since they do not alter the predictions made by the theories. Some are merely a difference in appreciation for the "window dressing" involved in the formulation of physical theories. Others refer to the philosophical and theological consequences of the physical theories. The author is of the opinion that these consequences have sometimes been grossly exaggerated. Finally, some disagreements refer to the influence of modern science upon man's world view. Though it cannot be denied that science has changed our outlook in many respects, the author is of the opinion that a scientific world view, that is a set of concepts that can guide and command man's actions, has no place in science, but lies outside of it.

The formulation of the theological aspects of the problem has been strongly influenced by Professor Karl Barth's "Kirchliche Dogmatik." The author acknowledges the great help that this monumental work has given him in clarifying his theological thinking and in helping him to see the relationship (or better, the lack of relationship) between science and theology.

The author is indebted to Prof. Paul Holmer, the Rev. R. C. Beisel and the Rev. Dr. George Hall for reading the manuscript and suggesting improvements. Mrs. van der Ziel typed the manuscript.

—*The Author*

CONTENTS

CHAPTER ONE

The Nature of Scientific Inquiry and of The Christian Message

1. The nature of scientific inquiries[1-2-3]*

In defining what science is and aims at one must be careful not to use "loaded" definitions and labels. One should also use broad and open definitions instead of narrow ones, to allow for the great variety in scientific activity that is going on. In addition it should always be borne in mind that science forms *part* but not the *whole* of human life and activity.

A first example of a loaded definition is the statement "Science is the pursuit of truth." This is correct, of course. No person who is engaged in a scientific investigation wants to pursue falsehood. It is a loaded definition, however, for it suggests that all that is not science is not true.

As a second example, consider the label "exact sciences" that has been given to the various natural sciences. Again, there is an amount of truth in this label, as we shall see later, but it is not the whole truth. Moreover, the label creates the false impression that all other sciences are inexact by comparison.

Some philosophical circles have labeled religion and reli-

---

*These numbers refer to the bibliography at the end of chapters.

gious thinking as "pre-scientific." In a sense that is correct, for man practiced religion long before he started to pursue the sciences. It suggests, however, that religion has now been superseded by science, that a scientific world view should take the place formerly occupied by religion.

Some authors give such a narrow definition of science that many fields of scientific inquiry, except their own of course, are excluded. This may help in bolstering one's ego, but it is much better to give a broad and open definition that applies to a great number of different fields but does not specify in detail how the investigation is done and what methods are applied. We thus *define science as a systematic investigation, interrelation and exposition of a certain field of human experience.*

A scientific investigation starts with gathering facts. What these "facts" are, depends upon the field of investigation and should therefore not be narrowed down any further. It should be understood, of course, that merely gathering facts is in itself no more a science than is collecting stamps or hunting trophies. What is *done* with the facts determines whether it is a science or a hobby. What makes it a science is the systematic investigation of the facts, their organization and interrelation.

This does not specify in detail how the investigation is to be done and what methods have to be applied. That depends on the field of investigation, for each field brings with it its own method of investigation. It is obvious to even the most casual observer that the methods of investigation used in history and physics show considerable differences in detail. They have in common the systematic investigation, organization, and interrelation of the facts, but differ in the facts themselves and in the methods of processing the data.

If such a broad definition of science is used, it is rather obvious that theology should be classified as a science. It is the task of the Christian Church to proclaim the Christian message. In carrying out this task, the Church has found it necessary to develop a Christian theology. That is, it has to give a systematic investigation of the sources of this message, a systematic exposition of its content and a systematic inter-relation of its elements. This makes it as genuine a scientific enterprise as history and physics.

The methods used in the investigation, interrelation and exposition of data are determined by the object of the scientific study and not by preconceived notions about science. I dislike expressions such as "the scientific method," especially if its use implies that the method of scientific investigation is fixed once and for all and that it is the same for all fields of human inquiry. Particularly objectionable is the use of this expression when it implies that any investigation that does not fit within its rather narrow framework is unscientific. Such a dogmatic attitude, the word "dogmatic" is here used in the popular sense and not in the theological one, has no place in science.

The natural sciences have as their domain the systematic investigation, interrelation and exposition of natural phenomena. One usually distinguishes between the biological sciences that deal with living materials and the non-biological sciences, such as physics, chemistry and astronomy, that deal primarily with non-living materials. The borderline between the various fields is rather fluid and they strongly influence each other.

What the natural sciences are and aim at will be discussed in this book. In doing so, one has to be aware of some general, important aspects of the problem.

In the first place, one must discuss the experimental and theoretical procedures followed in the natural sciences and the criteria of truth that are applied to them. It is here that the scientists can be, and usually are, in full agreement. True enough, sometimes there are differences of opinion in these matters but they are usually resolved sooner or later. Differences of opinions *here* have consequences for the predicted outcome of new observations or experiments and it can thus be decided clearly who was right and who was wrong.

In the second place, one must ask which of the concepts introduced during the development of the natural sciences are fundamental and which of them are merely useful and convenient. Differences of opinion in these matters do *not* change any of the predictions that can be made; they merely reflect differences in the evaluation of the same material. Nevertheless, asking and answering that question is important for pedagogical reasons. It helps to obtain the feeling that one has really understood the problem. It aids in resisting exaggerated claims about what the natural sciences have taught us.

In the third place, it must be asked whether some of the concepts introduced in one of the natural sciences may also have relevance in the other natural sciences or even in fields outside the natural sciences. Before one does so, however, it should be ascertained whether the concepts can really be applied. Otherwise, one ends up in nonsense and creates confusion instead of clarification. In addition it should be investigated carefully, whether the introduction of the concepts eliminates any part of the problem.

Let the latter be illustrated by an example outside the field of the natural sciences, viz. the psychological explanation of religion by some psychological schools. It should be readily admitted that all religions, including the Christian religion, have important psychological aspects and components. Neither should it be denied that some religious phenomena have indeed a psychological basis. To give a *complete psychological explanation* of religion implies, however, that psychological factors form its *only* basis. This would imply that there is no real knowledge of God and no true relationship to Him. Therefore such an attempt eliminates vital aspects of the Christian religion and it is not at all surprising that the results obtained are in direct conflict with it.

The three aspects just mentioned belong to the legitimate domain of the natural sciences, or, in fact, of any science. Many people are not satisfied with this, however. They want a *world view,* that is, a set of rules, concepts and relationships that can guide, direct and even command their actions and decisions. It has often been attempted to develop a "scientific world view," that is, a world view based upon the natural sciences. Some people have even considered this to be one of the major aims of the natural sciences. Nobody should be denied the privilege of doing this; it will be shown in Chapter 16 why this is not a part of the natural sciences but lies outside of it. For that reason these attempts do not carry the same authority and the same power of conviction that is carried by the methods of the natural sciences. Anybody who develops such a world view, does so at his own risk and should not claim the support of science.

2. The Christian message[4]

To explain in a few words the content of the Christian message is an almost impossible task. It has many aspects and it speaks in many different ways. To mention only some of the most important ones might distort the content of the message by leaving other important ones unmentioned. Nevertheless this chance must be taken.

The Christian message is the message of God's love toward men. It speaks of God's revelation, that is, of the acts in which God made and makes Himself known to man. Its center is God's act of making Himself known in Jesus Christ and for that reason it bears His name. The written record of this message is the Bible and as such the Bible plays *the* important part in the Christian Church.

God revealed Himself. We do not start by first proving that there is a God, then finding out more about Him and ultimately finding Him. That could have been the road by which God should be found; the hard fact that God revealed Himself indicates that it is not the road. The Christian message does not deal with the road that man makes to God, but with the road that God made toward man. That is its negative side. Its positive side is the assurance that God *is,* for He revealed Himself, that we can *know* Him, because that is the purpose of this revelation, and that the road to God is *open.*

The Bible speaks of God the Father, our Creator. We ask the questions: "What is the ground of our being?" "Does our life have a goal?" and "Does our life have a future?" That God revealed Himself as the Creator answers these questions in the affirmative. Yes, our being has a ground, for God created us, and hence this ground is in Him. Yes, our life has a goal, to love and to obey Him. Yes, our life has a future, the future with Him. But the hard fact is that we are not what we should be. We are sinners, we disobeyed Him and followed our own road. Thereby we cut ourselves from the ground of our being, from our goal and from our future.

The Bible speaks of God, the Son,* our Redeemer. Despite the fact that man was not true to God, God remained true to man. God came to man in Jesus Christ, to win him back. This fact is the center of the Christian message. In Christ God came to seek and to find us. In Christ's death He showed the depth of our rebellion as well as the height of His love. In Christ's resurrection He showed that His love is stronger than our sin, that our rebellion against Him is forgiven and that the relation between God and man is restored. For that reason the Apostle Paul could say: "God was in Christ reconciling the world unto Himself." From now on we have a task: not to believe and trust in ourselves, but to repent and believe and to trust God's love as shown in Jesus Christ.

What makes timid disciples into bold apostles, persecutors of the church into leaders of the church, unbelievers into believers? Not their own reason and strength, says the Bible, but the power of God's Holy Spirit. As Luther put it: "The Holy Spirit has called me by the gospel, enlightened me with His gifts, sanctified and kept me in the true faith." (Small Catechism). This implies that our own reason and strength are not enough. We need to be comforted by God's spirit and sustained by His strength.

To sum it up: the Christian message is the message of the *grace* of the triune God, Father, Son and Holy Spirit. The epistles of the Apostle Paul are one great hymn to the praise and the glory of this grace.

This message of God's love and grace is *preached.* Preaching is not lecturing about the message, nor weighing the pros and the cons of it. It means that the good news of God's love

---

*Those who have difficulty with the term "Son of God" are reminded of the fact that the New Testament uses the term "son of . . ." often in the sense of "of the kind of . . ." Seen from that angle, the term "Son of God" thus states that Jesus Christ is God (see also chapter 9 on the Trinity).

and grace is *proclaimed* in order to carry those that hear it along and, by the power of the Holy Spirit, bring them to the same faith in Jesus Christ. In science it is a commendable attitude not to be personally involved but to be open to all possibilities. The preaching of the Christian message, however, does not call man to sit on the fence but to make a decision of faith.

In preaching the Christian message the Church cannot give any *external* criteria of truth by which man can judge and decide whether or not the message is true. The proof is an *internal* one; the message gives what it promises to *those that believe it!*

The Christian message has social consequences. Though the primary aim of preaching the message is to bring a new relationship between God and man, it has as its consequences a new relationship among men. In the Christian preaching the believers are reminded of their high calling and they are called upon to demonstrate their faith in their behavior, especially in their relationship to others. Practically all the Epistles of the New Testament give examples of it. The Christian message is the seed, a demonstration of faith is the fruit.

The Christian message brings freedom. Since God has done all those things that man could not do himself, he is called upon to stop doing the impossible and set free to do what is possible. This freedom has many aspects; they include among other things a freedom for science. Some people have the mistaken idea that the Christian message hampers science. On the contrary, the Christian message sets man free, and this freedom extends to the field of science.*

---

*It is not denied that some churches have sometimes hampered scientific progress in the past. This reflects the fact that the Christian Churches do not always live up to the great freedom that they have in Jesus Christ.

In view of all this it is evident that the Christian message and the natural sciences have little in common; they complement each other. The Christian message is not dependent upon science, science can neither add to nor subtract from it.* There is neither a conflict between the two, nor a harmony, but a real difference.

*Though the Christian message as such is independent of science, our way of speaking about it may reflect our knowledge or ignorance about science. For example, a theological discussion may happen to contain references to earlier scientific concepts that have been discarded by responsible scientists. This has sometimes caused misunderstandings in the past. If the theologian is aware of the difficulty it is usually easy to remove it.

REFERENCES:

[1]Herbert Butterfield, Editor, *A Short History of Science*, Anchor Books, 1958.
[2]Stephan Toulmin, *A Philosophy of Science*, Hutchinson Univ. Library, 1955.
[3]A. N. Whitehead, *Science and the Modern World*, Mentor Books, New York, 1948.
[4]Karl Barth, *Kirchliche Dogmatik*, Evangelischer Verlag, Zollikon, Zürich.
Several volumes of the Kirchliche Dogmatik have appeared in English transition; translation of the remaining volumes is in progress.

CHAPTER TWO

Methods Used In The Natural Sciences

1. Observation, experiment, theory[1-2-3-5]

The first step in a scientific investigation is to gather facts. In the natural sciences that is done by observation and experiment. The reason for this was neatly summed up by an 18th century Dutch physicist, who wrote: "Since we have no innate knowledge of nature, we have to investigate all things diligently." The next step is to interrelate different phenomena and to present them in a generalized and unified form; in the natural sciences that is the task of the theory.

Many observations can already be done with the unaided human senses. Especially in the past, the classification of the external and the gross internal structure of animals or plants was an important part of zoology or botany. Much more information can be obtained, however, by extending the human means of observation. A biologist uses a microscope for the study of the more detailed structure of animals and plants. If that is not sufficient, he has at his disposal powerful electron microscopes that allow him to study down to the level of large molecules. In physics the field electron microscope and the field ion microscope allow the scientist to study the structure of surfaces down to the atomic level. In astronomy powerful optical and radio telescopes extend the range of our observations to galaxies so far away that it takes the light more than a billion years to travel the distance.

In some scientific investigations one can only *observe* what is going on, but one cannot interfere with the object under investigation. For example, in astronomy one can observe what goes on in the universe but one cannot (or, at least, not yet) change the course of events. In other sciences, however, one can *experiment;* that is, one can try to systematically change the conditions under which the phenomenon occurs, preferably one by one, and then observe the corresponding changes in the course of events. By experimentation one can usually learn many more features of the phenomenon, find what variables contribute to it, and thus begin to understand the causal relationships involved. Let me illustrate this with a puppet such as used in puppet shows. By casual observation one sees only the puppet and a number of wires attached to it. By pulling the wires one by one, one can learn which wire moves a certain part of the puppet and so begin to understand its detailed operation.

Difficulties arise if the observed phenomena are not fully reproducible. This is an indication that uncontrolled factors contribute to the outcome of the results. One then has to find these uncontrolled factors and start controlling them. The aim is always to obtain results that are reproducible within the limit of accuracy of the experiment. This is important for two reasons. In the first place, a fact can only be trusted if it can be verified at a later date by the original investigator or by others. In the second place, results of different experiments can only be interrelated if they are reproducible.

In some fields of the natural sciences the information is more or less qualitative. As such it is not unimportant, however. For example, it is already an interesting bit of astronomical information that distant galaxies recede from us. A more detailed study shows that the galaxies recede with a speed proportional to their distance. This is more important than the mere statement that the galaxies recede, for it gives an important clue to what may be going on (Chapter 13). To sum it up, one may say that in qualitative investigations one asks the question "how," in quantitative investigations one asks the questions "how many" or "how much."

Quantitative knowledge means that physical phenomena are expressed in terms of *numbers*. The operations needed for obtaining these numbers are known as *measurements*. The saying, "knowledge through measurement," adequately describes one of the chief tools of the natural sciences. Since physical quantities are thus expressed in terms of numbers, relations between quantities are usually relations between numbers. But relations between numbers are the domain of mathematics. This makes it understandable why mathematics plays such an important role in many of the natural sciences. The relationship between physical quantities are thus expressed as mathematical relationships. For example, Newton's law of gravitation states that the attractive force between two masses is proportional to each of the masses and inversely proportional to the square of the distance between them. This mathematical formulation comes at the end of the investigation, after sufficient data have been gathered, organized and related.

To interrelate different phenomena and thus arrive at a unified body of information is the task of the theory. There are two types of theories: phenomenological theories and theories based upon hypotheses. A phenomenological theory interrelates known facts and is mainly descriptive. It starts from a few well-established facts and relates other facts to them. The theory of electromagnetism is a good example of it. In a theory based upon hypotheses the scientist makes one or more hypotheses not necessarily based upon direct evidence, and relates a whole body of facts back to these hypotheses. The interrelation between the facts is now an indirect one; it goes via the hypotheses. The special theory of relativity, as originally introduced by Einstein, is such a theory. "Theoretical explanations" in the natural sciences thus mean one of two things. Either the theory relates new phenomena back to a few hypotheses, or the theory relates the phenomena back to earlier well-established facts. If a scientist claims: "We do not make hypotheses," he is either mistaken or he is talking about a phenomenological theory.

The dividing line between the two types of theory is sometimes difficult to draw. Bohr's theory of the light emission from hydrogen atoms is based upon three postulates, but these postulates merely describe what must be done to make the theory fit the data. Sometimes a theory based on hypotheses can later be reformulated as a phenomenological theory. The tendency during the last few hundred years has been to put the theories on a phenomenological, descriptive basis. Only in the field of cosmology, where the evidence is scarce and the extrapolations are long, are the hypotheses flourishing as in the days of old.

Since the interrelations between natural phenomena are usually expressed as mathematical interrelations, the theories are usually *mathematical theories*. There are exceptions, of course, especially in sciences where the use of mathematics is not well developed. In those cases the theory interrelates and unifies the phenomena in a non-mathematical manner. For example, the theory of evolution is a grand attempt to interpret the succession of the various forms of animal life and plant life in the past as an actual kinship and the present stage of animal and plant life as the result of a long development.

2. Interrelation between theory and experiment

We saw that the mathematical formulation of an experimental investigation came at the end of the investigation, after the data had been assembled, unified and interrelated. Such a mathematical formulation is known as a *law*. A law is much more than the sum of the few or many data taken; what was found to be true several times is postulated to be true at all times. Often the formulation of the law allows new conclusions to be drawn from it. It should then be verified whether these conclusions agree with the experimental evidence. It should also be investigated whether there might be conditions under which a law does not hold. As a matter of fact, new developments in physics have often come from the discovery that certain seemingly well-established laws could be violated under certain conditions.

The starting point of an investigation is usually an experimental one. This is especially the case if one has to do with a new phenomenon about which no past experimental evidence is available and for which either no theory exists, or for which the theoretical situation is obscure. If earlier evidence is available, one usually starts by studying this evidence from the available publications and then tries to find the means by which fresh experimental evidence can be obtained. If the existing theories might be applicable, it may still be important to start with experimental work since that may give further clues as to the *direction* in which the theory should be applied. In some cases the predictions of the existing theories are very precise and clearcut and further experiments are either unnecessary or merely serve as an additional check of the theory.

In some cases the interrelation between the phenomena is a relatively simple one, and very few, properly chosen, data are sufficient to start an intelligent theory. In other cases the interrelation is a very complex one and a large number of data are needed before one can even hope to develop a successful theory. One often starts out with the assumption that the relationship is a simple one, develops a theory, predicts the outcome of new experiments and tries to verify these predictions. If they are verified, then the theory has withstood another test and is more firmly established. If some predictions are not satisfied, one must investigate carefully the cause of the discrepancy and remove it by means of an appropriate change in the theory. If none of the predictions are satisfied, this is a clear indication that the situation was much more complex than originally anticipated. Many more independent data are then needed, before theoretical considerations become worth while.

Sometimes a new phenomenon does not fit into the existing framework and the existing theories cannot explain it. This means that the theoretical basis for dealing with the phenomenon is not yet available. It may take a long time before such an undesirable condition is eliminated. For example, Balmer established his formula for the hydrogen spectrum in 1882, but it lasted until 1913 before Bohr developed the theory for it. It was discovered in 1911 that the electrical resistance of some metals becomes zero at low temperatures; this effect is known as superconductivity. A theory that can explain such a behavior was developed only in 1957.

There is thus an intimate interconnection between experiment and theory. Experiments act as a guide and a basis for the theory and theory acts as a guide and a basis for further experiments. The aim is always to obtain agreement between the two within the limits of experimental accuracy. Theory without experiments and experiments without theory are threatened with sterility. The intimate interplay between both is responsible for the spectacular progress in the natural sciences during the last few centuries.

Since most scientists are either experimentalists or theorists, it sometimes happens that there is a lack of understanding between both groups and not enough appreciation for the position of the other group. Such a situation may hamper scientific progress considerably. We shall see later that there is a parallel situation in theology.

3. The use of mathematics in the natural sciences

There is nothing mysterious about the use of mathematics in science. It comes about everywhere where quantitative determinations are made and quantitative predictions aimed at. For that reason I must take exception to the view of the famous British astronomer and theoretical physicist Jeans who maintained that this had important philosophical and theological implications. According to Jeans the use of mathematics in modern science indicated that "the Architect of the Universe is a great mathematician." In my opinion modern theoretical physics merely shows that physicists have become good mathematicians. I do not want to sound impious, but I suspect that this "mathematician-architect of the Universe," deduced from modern physics, is nothing but a projection of an idealized mathematical physicist against the sky and has nothing to do with the God about Whom the Christian message speaks. Christians should not try to make apologetical capital out of this role of mathematics. In our discussion of mechanics in

Chapter 3 we shall see the dangers involved in such an attempt.

The use of mathematics presupposes that knowledge about the phenomena under study is already available. It is possible, but not very useful, to hide our ignorance about a new phenomenon behind mathematical symbols. Unfortunately such a procedure is not uncommon. Mathematics can be useful if the physical processes involved can be formulated. If a new relationship cannot be stated clearly in words, it makes little sense to express it mathematically. The director of the division of a big research lab where I worked always used the yardstick: "If you cannot state your results in plain language, you have not understood them yourself." It is among the most valuable pieces of advice that I have ever received.

At present there are sciences where mathematics is used as a regular tool and other sciences where this is not the case. In a certain field where mathematics is not used as a tool *now,* it may become an important tool *later.* One might think here of the increasing part that various branches of mathematics, especially statistics, begin to play in economics. The author is inclined to think that there will always be fields of human inquiry where mathematics is important and other fields where it is unimportant, even though a particular field may be shifted from the latter to the former group when times goes on. The use or non-use of mathematics is not necessarily a property of the field under study but more likely it is inherent to the present nature of our inquiry. It is hard to imagine, however, that mathematics will ever become an important tool in history or in theology.

4. Experimental and theoretical accuracy. Errors[4].

The name "exact sciences" does not describe the natural

sciences adequately. For the data obtained are only approximately correct and the theories developed have only limited validity. In some cases the determination of the order of magnitude of a certain quantity is already an important achievement. In other cases a certain quantity can be measured with an accuracy better than one part per million. But irrespective of how accurately one measures, there is always *some* limitation to the accuracy. In the same way theories have only limited validity. For example, classical mechanics is inapplicable to particles that have velocities comparable with the velocity of light. It is also invalid in the atomic domain.

It is always the goal of the natural sciences to improve the accuracy of the data and to generalize the existing theories. Exactness, however, implies *unlimited* accuracy of the data and *unlimited* validity of the theories. At best that is a goal that can only be achieved after an infinitely long time interval, or to use theological terminology: "Exactness in the natural sciences is an eschatological concept." Additional limitations exist in the atomic domain, as will be seen in our discussion of wave mechanics.

As mentioned before, measurements are subject to errors. One distinguishes between *random* errors and *systematic* errors. This distinction will be illustrated with the help of an example. Suppose one shoots with a gun at a distant target for a number of times and notes where the bullets hit the target. One observes that the bullets do not all hit the same point but that the hits spread around an average position. The spread comes about, because one cannot aim the gun perfectly and because the initial speed and direction of the bullet, when coming out of the barrel, are not quite the same for different shots. These errors are *random* errors. In addition it may happen that the average position of the hits does not coincide with the point aimed at. This may be caused by the fact that the barrel of the gun is slightly crooked or by the effect of the wind upon the path of the bullet. These are *systematic* errors; they can be eliminated by straightening the gun barrel and by taking the influence of the wind velocity into account.

In order to make more accurate measurements one must reduce the random errors and eliminate the systematic ones. The latter can be done by a careful analysis of the factors contributing to the final result, as shown in our example. Since there is always a possibility that one of the factors is not taken into account, it is advisable to measure the quantity in question by more than one method. For example, if two independent measurements, each with an accuracy of 1%, give results that deviate by 10%, it is rather obvious that there were systematic errors. These then must be traced and eliminated.

The random errors in a measurement are caused by inaccuracies in the reading of the instruments used for the measurement. It is obvious that they can be reduced by taking more accurate measurements. Greater improvement is sometimes possible by introducing more accurate measuring methods. We shall illustrate this with two examples. Suppose one wants to measure a certain quantity a that has a value close to unity and suppose the direct measurement can be carried out with 1% accuracy. By designing a method for measuring $(1 - a)$ with an accuracy of 1% (suppose that can be done), a is determined much more accurately than by the former method. A second interesting example is the so-called "null-method," where one compares the difference between an unknown quantity and a variable known quantity and adjusts the latter until their difference is zero.

The random errors can also be reduced by repeating the measurement many times and taking the average of all the results. As a matter of fact, it may be shown that if the measurement is repeated n times and if the measurements are independent, then the inaccuracy in the average is $(1/\sqrt{n})$ times the inaccuracy of a single measurement. It thus takes an infinitely long time to obtain an exact result, as mentioned before.

One of the main reasons for improving the accuracy of the measurements is that it often allows one to detect small effects that cannot be explained by the existing theory. For the laws are only known as far as the measuring accuracy permits. Effects that give a contribution smaller than the random errors in the measurement are not detected. Increasing the accuracy may mean that some of these effects become detectable.

In some respects one might wonder why theoretical physics is possible at all. We know that we live in a complex universe. If everything interacted strongly with everything, the physical laws would be so complex that we would not be able to formulate them mathematically. Fortunately practically all interactions are extremely weak. If no great accuracy is required, few interactions need be taken into account and the "laws" are often quite simple. If greater accuracy is needed, more interactions must be taken into account and the "laws" become more complex.

The inaccuracy of our knowledge is thus not necessarily a drawback; it is initially an asset. Progress in the natural sciences would have been slower if the first measurements had not been rather inaccurate. Inaccurate measurements allow only the detection of the simplest of laws and lead to the simplest theories. Increasing the accuracy step by step increases the number of interactions that have to be taken into account, corresponding to an increased complexity of the mathematical problem.

5. Different levels of understanding[4]

We saw in the last section that increasing the accuracy of the measurement might lead to a deeper understanding. It should now be pointed out that in the natural sciences there are also different levels of understanding based upon probing deeper and deeper into the problems. We shall give here a few examples from physics.

In 19th century physics properties like the melting point of solids, the boiling point of liquids, the electrical resistance of conductors, the strength of materials, etc., which are all quantities of great importance in engineering applications, occurred only as material constants. By probing deeper into these problems, physicists are gradually learning how to explain these properties from the structure of these materials. The ultimate aim is the accurate explanation of the physical properties of the existing materials and the prediction of the properties of future materials. This has already led to important technical applications with many more to be expected.

One can put this as follows: In one level of understanding the properties of the materials are considered to be a consequence of the properties of its molecules, but the properties of the latter are not the object of further study (molecular theories). In the next level the properties of the molecules are a consequence of the properties of the atoms from which the molecules are built (molecular structure). In a still deeper level of understanding the properties of the atoms are attributed to their structure, that is, to the fact that the atom consists of a positively charged nucleus surrounded by negatively charged electrons (atomic theory). The following step is to study this structure and to attribute the properties of the nucleus to the protons and neutrons that are part of it and to the mutual interaction between these elementary particles (nuclear theory). The next logical step is to explain this mutual interaction and to find out why there are particles like protons, neutrons and electrons and why they have those properties. And so it goes on.

How long will it continue? Time and again some prominent physicists have claimed that the end of it was in sight and time and again they were proved to be wrong. Up to now there always seemed to be something new around the corner. This has led other physicists to believe that this may go on forever, that there is an infinite number of levels of investigation, probing deeper and deeper into nature. Who knows who is right and who is wrong? This problem has no solution. It is somewhat naive, however, to believe that we know already practically everything. Since we do not know yet what we do not know, it is sensible to be prepared for the possibility that there is much more to be learned.

6. Diversification and unification in the natural sciences[6]

As the natural sciences expand, large new areas are opened up for further research. At present it is not sufficient to divide the natural sciences up into the four main branches of astronomy, physics, chemistry and biology, but each of these branches is subdivided into an ever-growing number of different fields. Most scientists are only competent in one rather narrow field. People competent in several fields become scarcer every day, which is one of the bad features of this rapid expansion. If there were no other side to the story, this development might lead to the atomization of science itself.

Fortunately, the story has another side. Time and again new connections are made between the various fields. For example, several links have been established between physics and astronomy; celestial mechanics has linked astronomy and mechanics, astrophysics has connected astronomy and atomic physics, nuclear physics has laid the basis for an understanding of the source of energy supply in stars. Links have also been established between physics and chemistry. For example, the quantum-mechanical theory of the chemical bond has given a physical basis for the binding forces between the atoms that are responsible for the great variety of chemical compounds. Biochemistry has linked chemistry and biology, biophysics has linked physics and biology. The quantum theory in physics seems to be able to provide an understanding for the elementary processes governing mutations. We will come back to all these problems later.

There are always two dangers coming from opposite directions. The one danger is not of seeing that the concepts and the data are already at hand that allow to unify two fields. The opposite danger is to unify them prematurely. We live in a complex universe and it would be rather strange if a single idea or a single principle would be universally valid and would form the basis of all the natural sciences. One must be even more careful if the desire for unification extends itself over other fields of human experience.

Let me illustrate this as follows. One can get a very clear idea of a picture by looking at it from one point of view. If one wants to buy a house, however, one is not satisfied with looking at the front, but one wants to walk around it, through it and look at it from the inside out and from the outside in. Only by looking at it from many different angles can one get a good idea of what the house is really like.

The same is true in the natural sciences. In simple cases it is possible to get a good idea of the problem by looking at it from one point of view. In more complicated cases one may have to look at the problem from different points of view and let these points of view complement each other. The better one wants to understand the problem, the larger the number of different views that may have to be taken. For that reason one should always be open to the possibility that another point of view might complement the understanding of the problem.

If this is already necessary in the natural sciences, it is even more so if one looks at all the fields of human experience and understanding together. To get the full understanding of all the various problems, many different, complementary views are needed. This should be a warning against all attempts to develop complete and closed systems of thinking that are the basis of many "scientific world views." In such a system the world in which we live and move has been simplified to such an extent that major fields of human experience have simply disappeared. What is completely lacking here is an openness to these points of view and a refusal to be enlightened by them.

This applies, for example, to the problem of science and religion. It is never solved by abandoning the one in favor of the other, or by molding the one so that it is more compatible with the other. What is needed is that one listens to both points of view, permits them to complement each other and allows each to apply itself in its proper way.

7. Facts, hypotheses and speculations

Popular books, magazines and newspapers sometimes present science in a distorted form. One of the commonest distortions is that no distinction is made between facts, hypotheses and speculations. Sometimes one reads: "Science tells us . . ."

and then one of the wildest speculations ever made is treated as a proved fact. The ideas found in the natural sciences cover the full range from speculation to hypothesis to fact. On the basis of presently available evidence it is usually not difficult to decide whether a certain idea falls into the one category or the other. This does not imply, of course, that what is a wild speculation now, may not become a well-established fact later. On the contrary, this has often happened in the past.

Let us make the following distinctions in science. Something will be called a *fact* if there is direct, irrefutable evidence in favor of it. It will be called *probable* if the evidence is strong, but not irrefutable. It will be called *possible,* if it is one of the several interpretations or conclusions that is compatible with the existing data. It will be called *improbable* if there is some, not fully irrefutable, evidence against it. It will be called *impossible* if there is direct, irrefutable evidence against it. All this, of course, under the restriction: based upon evidence presently available.

Something will be called an *hypothesis* if it is one of the *assumptions,* not directly based upon experimental evidence, upon which a successful theory can be based. A statement will be called a *speculation* if it is a possibility but with little or no evidence in its favor.*

Let me illustrate this. There is, in my opinion, irrefutable scientific evidence that the earth is about 4.5 billion years old (Chapter 12). There is also strong, but not completely irrefutable scientific evidence that the universe is expanding and that galaxies move away from ours with a speed proportional to their distance to us. When this expanding motion is extrapo-

---

*The existing nomenclature is presently under serious discussion; especially words like "facts," "theories," "models," "laws," etc. are being reassessed (compare e.g. Hutton's book)[7].

lated back into the past, everything is found to have been close together almost five billion years ago. This is, of course, an interesting coincidence, but it might be accidental; one must be careful with such long extrapolations. If all matter had been so close together in the remote past, very peculiar things could have happened. There are several theories about what *might* have happened, but these theories have a less firm basis than the theory of the expanding universe or the age determination of the earth. Some of them should presently be classified as interesting speculations.

There is another distortion. Under the heading "Science tells us . . ." one sometimes encounters statements that are made possible because a mathematical method of representing the facts is taken as a reality. Statements like: "The only real quantities in electromagnetics are the electric and the magnetic fields," or: "We live in a four-dimensional space-time continuum" belong in this category. These statements usually cause more confusion than clarification about the aims of modern science.

These is still another distortion. Sometimes one encounters the expression: "Science tells us . . ." and what follows is not a conclusion of science but a conclusion based upon a "scientific world view." It should be clearly understood that such a conclusion is not a scientific one.

This is of interest to theologians. A scientific fact, theory or speculation should never bother a theologian who is sure of the foundations of his theology, though it is important to know whether one has to do with the one or the other. A scientific world view, just as any other world view, aims at capturing the hearts and minds of people, and as such enters into direct competition with the Christian message. To attack science would be foolish, to answer a world view, whether or not it claims to be scientific, may be highly necessary. We will come back to this later.

REFERENCES:

[1]James B. Conant, *On Understanding Science*, Mentor Books, New York, 1951.

[2]P. W. Bridgeman, *The Nature of Physical Theory*, Dover Publications, New York, 1936.

[3]M. Born, *Experiment and Theory in Physics*, Dover Publications, New York, 1956.

[4]D. Bohm, *Causality and Chance in Modern Physics*, Routledge and Kegan Paul Ltd., London, 1957.

[5]Ph. Frank, *Philosophy of Science*, Prentice Hall, Englewood Cliffs, N. J., 1957.

[6]A. d'Arbro, *The Evolution of Scientific Thought*, Dover Publications, New York, 1951.

[7]L. Hutton, *The Language of Modern Physics*, Allen and Unwin, London, Macmillan, New York, 1956.

Mechanics

Mechanics was one of the parts of classical physics that was first developed. One usually speaks of Newtonian mechanics, since Newton was the first to put its basic principles in its present form. Actually it was the *end point* of a long development to which many scientists contributed. At the same time it was also the starting point of a very intensive application of mathematics to physical problems.

1. Newton's laws of mechanics[1-5]

Newton's laws can be formulated as follows:

I. A body persists in its condition of rest or uniform rectilinear motion unless acted upon by a force.

II. A force F acting upon a body produces an acceleration a in the direction of the force such that:
$$F = ma, \qquad (1)$$
where m is the mass of the body.

III. Action equals reaction. If two bodies exert forces upon one another, then these forces have equal magnitude and opposite direction.

There is a whole development behind these simple laws. They are by no means obvious, but are the consequence of a considerable extrapolation of the observations and even seem to contradict everyday experience. For it is common knowledge that usually a force is needed to produce uniform motion. Everybody knows that the motor of the car has to be kept running to maintain a constant speed of the car. At first one might thus think that a force maintains a *velocity* and not a *change in velocity* or acceleration. The effect is caused by *friction;* a force is needed to overcome the frictional forces. One can thus only come to the true laws of motion by extrapolating to the case of zero friction. It took considerable experience and imagination to take this important step.

The idea that a force produces a velocity is also behind a reasoning given by St. Thomas Aquinas which we quote: "Whatever is in motion is moved by another: and it is clear to the sense that something, the sun for instance, is in motion. Therefore, it is set in motion by something else moving it. Now that which moves is in itself either moved or not. If it be not moved, then the point is proved that we must needs postulate an immovable mover: and this we call God. If, however, it be moved, it is moved by another mover. Either, therefore, we must proceed to infinity or we must come to an immovable mover. But it is not possible to proceed to infinity. Therefore, it is necessary to postulate an immovable mover."*

This quotation shows what far-reaching conclusions medieval philosophers drew from the simple observable fact that "something" is needed to produce motion. It indicates how intimately science, philosophy and theology were connected together in those days. It makes it understandable how difficult it

*Quoted from Ph. Frank, *Philosophy of Science*, l.c., pp. 94-95.

must have been to gain the insight that ideally *no force is needed* to produce uniform motion and that in actual cases a force is needed only to overcome friction. Finally, the close tie-up between medieval theology and science makes it understandable why revolutionary changes in the latter were bound to have far-reaching consequences for the former. We will come back to this later.

The quantities introduced in the formulation of Newton's laws of mechanics require a more careful definition. The velocity of *uniform* rectilinear motion is defined as the ratio s/t, where s is the distance traveled during the time t. For non-uniform rectilinear motion the time is divided into small time intervals Δt and the distance Δs traveled during this time interval is determined. The *average* velocity v_{av} is now defined as:

$$v_{av} = \Delta s/\Delta t \qquad (2)$$

If Δt is taken small enough, v_{av} will be practically independent of Δt. Mathematically, the value of the instantaneous velocity v is now defined as the limit approached by v_{av} if Δt goes to zero. It is written as:

$$v = \lim_{\Delta t \to 0} \Delta s/\Delta t = ds/dt \qquad (2a)$$

The speedometer of a car works essentially on this principle.

If the instantaneous velocity v changes with time, the body is said to be *accelerated* or *decelerated*, depending on whether the velocity increases or decreases. The change Δv in instantaneous velocity during the time Δt is now determined and the average acceleration a_{av} is defined as:

$$a_{av} = \Delta v/\Delta t \qquad (3)$$

Mathematically, the instantaneous acceleration a is defined as the limit approached by a_{av} if Δt goes to zero:

$$a = \lim_{\Delta t \to 0} \Delta v / \Delta t = dv/dt = d^2s/dt^2 \qquad (3a)$$

No definition is given of a force, but an appeal is made to everyday experience. The mass m is introduced as a proportionality factor, connecting an intuitively known concept, the force F, and a well-defined concept, the acceleration a. The mass m reflects the fact that the *same* force acting on different bodies produces different accelerations. This difference is taken into account by introducing the mass m as a property of the body.

2. The differential equation method. The well-ordered universe[1].

The above definitions have already illustrated how mathematics is used in the definition of velocity and acceleration. To indicate how mathematical physics is developed from here we consider a body of mass m moving along a straight line. Let the body be at a distance s_0 from a fixed point of reference at the instant $t = t_0$ and let v_0 be its instantaneous velocity at that time. Let s be the distance to the fixed point of reference at the instant t. Let the force F acting upon the body depend upon its position, this is indicated by writing $F = F(s)$. Newton's second law of motion may then be written:

$$m \ d^2s/dt^2 = F(s) \qquad (4)$$

Equation (4) is known as a *differential* equation; the mathematical methods for solving it are well developed. It may be shown mathematically that such an equation has *one and only one solution* if the initial position and velocity of the mass point are given. In our case they were:

$$s = s_0 \text{ and } v = v_0 \text{ at } t = t_0 \qquad (4a)$$

This mathematical result agrees with everyday experience. People that go hunting make use of it. If the gun is right and proper aim is taken, the hunter will hit the target he aims at.

The same procedure is followed in the solution of any mechanical problem. The first question is: "What are the forces acting upon the system?" and the next question is: "What are the initial conditions?" If these questions have been answered, the physical problem has been reduced to a mathematical one.

A similar pattern is followed in all parts of mathematical physics. The first question is: "What are the laws?" and the second is: "What are the initial conditions?" By expressing the laws in the form of differential equations, and that can always be done, the physical problem is reduced to a mathematical one. Solving the mathematical problem allows to predict the future behavior of the physical system under consideration. *The laws and the initial conditions thus completely determine future behavior.* This is the scientific basis of 18th and 19th century *determinism.* I do not necessarily mean that it is the *only* basis.

How firm is this scientific basis? That depends on the answer to the following question: "How accurately do we know the laws and the initial conditions?" This answer determines the accuracy of our theoretical predictions. As mentioned before, we do not know the *exact* initial conditions and we do not know the *exact* laws. All we know are approximations, sometimes good ones, sometimes poor ones. For any determination of the initial conditions is subject to random errors and the laws are only known in-as-far as the measuring accuracy permits. *Exact prediction is only possible for the mathematical model representing the physical system, not for the system itself.* The scientific basis of determinism is thus none too firm.

As mentioned before, increasing the accuracy of the measurements may lead to the discovery of effects that had hitherto escaped notice. These effects show up as small additional terms in the differential equations. The more complex mathematical problem that results can be solved by so-called "perturbation methods." In these methods one first solves the differential equation without the additional terms and then makes a correction for these small terms. It may be shown that accurate predictions, with the help of these methods, can only be made over time intervals that are not too long. For the more distant future they may become quite unreliable.

The development of mathematical physics led to the conclusion that our universe was a well-ordered universe where everything went according to fixed laws. Did not this order and these laws seem to indicate the existence of an all-powerful Creator, who created and maintained it all? Many scientists and theologians in the 17th and 18th centuries thought so and looked upon the natural sciences as a valuable or even necessary support of theology. This development was made possible for three reasons:

1. One did not realize the approximate character of these laws and this order.

2. One overlooked the possibility that at least part of this order might be imposed upon nature by the methods of investigation.

3. One had started to lose sight of the actual and only basis of Christian theology: faith and revelation.

This "victory" of theology was a very hollow one. For if the laws are fixed and the initial conditions are known, the future behavior is fully predictable. The job of this Creator was only to set the initial conditions and then let go. Everything was predictable from there on so that there was no need for a Creator to maintain it. The role of the Creator had become that of a retired engineer looking with satisfaction at his smoothly running, perfect world machine. But this seemed to strike at the heart of the Christian concept of the Creator as the Maintainer of His creation. Newton made feeble attempts to point out the necessity of a Maintainer of the universe by indicating that God was needed to prevent and to repair small perturbations and irregularities of the world machine. This led to Leibniz's sneering question whether the Almighty Creator could perchance have produced an imperfect world machine.

This development seems to point to the following conclusions:

a) The natural sciences are not a good starting point for Christian theology. Its starting point is the Christian message, not science.

b) The Christian concept of the Creator of the world as its Maintainer is primarily a non-mechanical concept.

c) The methods of the natural sciences should not be extended beyond its range of applicability.

3. Newton's law of gravitation. Unification of terrestrial and celestial mechanics[1].

Newton not only put the laws of mechanics in its present form, he also formulated the law of gravitation and explained the laws of planetary motion by unifying terrestrial and celestial mechanics. This was a bold departure from medieval thinking which always stressed the difference between the (imperfect) terrestrial phenomena and the (perfect) celestial phenomena.

Newton's formulation of the law of gravitation developed from Kepler's laws of planetary motion. Kepler had formulated these laws as follows:*

1. Planets describe ellipses around the sun with the sun in one of its focal points.

2. The radius vector, that is the line drawn from the sun to the planet, sweeps out equal areas of the ellipse in equal time intervals.

3. The squares of the periods of revolution of the planets are proportional to the cubes of the major axes of the ellipses.

Newton developed his theory of planetary motion as follows. He first showed that Kepler's second law holds for all motions caused by a central force, that is, a force directed toward a fixed center. Hence, Kepler's *second* law indicates that a planet is acted upon by a force directed toward the sun. He then showed that the orbit is an ellipse if the force is inversely proportional to the square of the distance to the center. He therefore concluded from Kepler's *first* law that the sun attracts the planet with a force that is inversely proportional to the square of the distance to the sun. According to Newton's third law the planet thus attracts the sun with a force of equal magnitude but the opposite direction. Kepler's third law follows automatically from Newton's laws of mechanics and from this force law.

Newton then enunciated the universal law of gravitation, according to which two masses m_1 and m_2 attract each other with a force that is inversely proportional to the square of their distance r. There is thus no basic difference between the force

---

*This was already quite a revolutionary set of laws. Medieval philosophers believed that heavenly bodies could only have heavenly (perfect) motion. Perfect motion meant for them that these bodies could only move in circles.

with which the earth attracts a stone and makes it fall to the ground and the force with which the earth attracts the moon and makes it describe an ellipse around the earth. Since the magnitude of the force with which the earth attracts a stone is proportional to its mass, the attractive force between two masses, m_1 and m_2, must be proportional to both m_1 and m_2. The universal law of gravitation may thus be written:

$$F = f\, m_1\, m_2 / r^2 \qquad (5)$$

The proportionality factor f was determined later in the laboratory.

Nowhere does Newton "explain" gravitation; he only drew the necessary conclusions from the data. For that reason he could proudly say: "We do not make hypotheses." Readers of his books will discover that he actually loved nothing better than making hypotheses, so that his restraint must have constituted a considerable self-denial. Huygens and Leibniz severely criticized Newton for the fact that he did not develop physical models that could explain gravitation. Actually, Newton's attitude is quite modern. At present the first task of the natural sciences is considered to describe and to relate. Only after this is done should an attempt be made to explain the results in terms of a deeper lying cause. This step has not yet been made for gravitation, so that Newton should not be blamed for his attitude, but instead should be commended.

The theory of planetary motion gives an illustration of perturbation methods. In first approximation the interaction of the planets may be neglected and only the force between the sun and the planet must be taken into account. In the next higher approximation the interaction with the other planets is taken into account. In that case the calculations become much more complex and the results allow only accurate prediction for time intervals that are not arbitrarily long.

4. Maximum and minimum principles. The "economical" universe[2-3].

After the laws of mechanics had been formulated, rapid developments took place in the natural sciences. One reason was that the liberation of science from the domination by philosophy and theology had emphasized the necessity of experimentation. Consequently, the body of known facts and established theories grew steadily and rapidly. The theory was stimulated by important mathematical discoveries that greatly extended the arsenal of mathematical tools available to the theoreticians.

One of the most interesting of the newly developed branches of mathematics was the calculus of variations. It allowed to formulate the laws of physics in terms of maximum and minimum principles. It is interesting not only from a mathematical point of view, but also because of the theological motivation behind it. This is especially clear in the case of Leibniz, one of the leaders in this development.

Let us quote him here directly:* "We must be able to give a reason why things must exist so and not otherwise. Now this sufficient reason for the existence of the Universe cannot be found in the series of contingent things . . . but must be outside the series of contingent things and be found in a substance which is its cause, or which is a necessary being, carrying the reason of its existence within itself; otherwise we should

---

*Leibniz, "The principles of nature and grace, based upon reason." (From Philip P. Wiener, Leibniz, Selections, pg. 527-529.) The title of this booklet shows the rationalistic character of Leibniz's thinking. It is rationalism in the service of his theology.

still not have a sufficient reason in which we could rest. And the final reason of things is called God.

"This primitive simple substance must contain in itself eminently the perfection contained in the derivative substances which are its effects (Leibniz means here the creatures created by God). Thus it will have perfect power, knowledge and will; that is, it will have supreme omnipotence, omniscience and goodness . . . and justice. . . . The reason which has caused things to exist by him makes them still dependent upon him in existing and in working; but the imperfection which remains in them, comes from the essential and original limitation of the creature.

"It follows from the supreme perfection of God, that in creating the Universe he has chosen *the best possible plan, in which there is the greatest variety together with the greatest order, the best arranged ground, place, time; the most results produced in the most simple ways;* the most of power, knowledge, happiness and goodness in the creatures that the Universe could permit. For since all the possibles in the understanding of God laid claim to existence in proportion to their perfection, the result of all these claims must be the most perfect actual world that is possible. And without this it would not be possible to give a reason why things have turned out so and not otherwise."

It is interesting to see how Leibniz managed to blend his theology, philosophy and science into a unity that has not been rivaled since. From here the program was clear: the laws of nature should be expressed in the form of maximum and minimum principles. That this expression of the laws of nature was at all *possible,* was considered to be a direct consequence of the theological concept of the supreme perfection of God.

On the other hand the *demonstrated* possibility of expressing the laws of nature in the form of maximum and minimum principles seemed to indicate the soundness of the theological concept and to show that indeed "the most results were produced in the most simple ways." Our universe is an "economical universe."

As an example of such a maximum and minimum consideration we discuss *Fermat's principle.* It says that when light travels from a point P_1 to a point P_2, then of all the possible paths connecting P_1 and P_2 the light ray takes the one that is traveled in the shortest time. This law holds for light rays traveling in free space and for the refraction of light rays by a lens. For the reflection of light rays against a mirror the principle has to be modified. Practically all the results of geometrical optics ($=$ the tracing of light rays) can be derived from it.

Such a description of a physical phenomenon by maximum and minimum principles, so-called "variational" principles, is known as a description by *variational methods.* In problems of this type one introduces a quantity that has a maximum or minimum value for the actual path taken. The quantity involved does not always have such a simple physical interpretation as in the case of Fermat's principle.

The efforts of Leibniz and his followers were highly successful. They have provided us with a useful mathematical tool: the calculus of variations. It may well be that this branch of mathematics would not have been developed so rapidly if those working on it had not been so strongly motivated by their theology. This should make us more tolerant toward scientists who have in our opinion the wrong motivation toward scientific research. Maybe just because of their wrong motivation they will develop something worth while. Not all scientists with a wrong motivation have Leibniz's genius, however.

It has sometimes been argued that the differential equation method stresses the laws and the initial conditions, so that it is *deterministic,* whereas the variational method stresses the laws and the end point (the goal), so that it is *teleological.* Unfortunately one can prove the following general theorem: *"Every problem that can be described by a differential equation can also be described by a variational principle and vice versa."* Since the two methods of mathematical description are thus identical, it is obvious that these branches of mathematical physics are unsuitable for discriminating between the deterministic and the teleological schools of thought.

Neither do these methods have any theological implications. They do not imply that this world is, or is not, the best possible. Neither do they prove, or disprove, that an Almighty Creator is behind it. They are nothing more than useful mathematical tools in the hands of theoretical physicists.

5. Use of these ideas in theology[5].

The quotation from St. Thomas might give the wrong impression that God was only a *postulate* in St. Thomas' arguments. Actually, he only used his arguments to build a framework that connected the natural life governed by reason with the supernatural life governed by revelation and grace. At most it acted as a bridge toward this supernatural life without being the basis of it. Neither should the quotation from Leibniz give the impression that God was only an *assumption* for Leibniz. He was a pious man, who developed his ideas connecting science, philosophy and theology in the defense of Christianity against the upcoming atheism. In contrast with St. Thomas, however, he did not put any Christian ideas into his system and for that reason he could not get any Christian idea out of it either. The man who understood this clearly was Pascal, who wrote in his "Memorial": "God of Abraham, God of Isaac, God of Jacob, not of the philosophers and scholars." The preface to the French edition of his "Pensees" quotes the following unpublished fragment:*

"I am not trying to prove here by natural reasoning either the existence of God, or the Trinity, or the immortality of the soul, nor anything of that nature; not only because I am not clever enough to find something in nature that can convince the hardened atheists, but also because this knowledge is useless and sterile without Jesus Christ." Many similar quotations could be given from the "Pensees" themselves.[6]

Leibniz was apparently not aware that his work did not prove what he had intended to prove. He intended it as a defense of Christianity. Did not his system start with the assumption that God was perfect and was not the existence of a perfect universe deduced as a conclusion from this assumption? Unfortunately this conclusion was not a direct consequence of this assumption. He could also have proved it directly from scientific principles by means of the calculus of variations. This step was taken by the theologian Christian Wolff, who first showed directly that the universe was perfect and then added that this was as expected in view of the perfection of God.

The French rationalists could then take the next step. They declared that the assumption of a perfect God was an unnecessary hypothesis, that could be eliminated from Leibniz' system. In this point of view they were correct. For they still maintained Leibniz's most important ideas: The supremacy of human reason and the perfect universe. Since these ideas were inde-

---

*Translated by the author.

pendent of Leibniz's assumption of a perfect God, they could rightly claim that they had eliminated only superfluous elements. By doing so, they had made it into a completely irreligious system, just the opposite of what Leibniz had intended.

Actually nothing was proved, except that Leibniz's starting point for developing and defending theology was not a good one. This lesson is a purely negative one, but as such it is not without value.

There is little *positive* use of the natural sciences in the defense of the Christian religion, neither for the "order" demonstrated in the universe, nor for the "economy" imagined by some. The positive defense of the Christian religion consists in telling what it *is*. The task of the theologian is not to search for real or imaginary links between science and Christianity but to do his work faithfully, with an open mind and from the only basis in which it can be done: the Christian message itself.

REFERENCES:

[1] E. J. Dijksterhuis, *Die Mechanisierung des Weltbildes*, Springer-Verlag, 1956.

[2] Philip P. Wiener, *Leibniz - Selections*, Scribner, New York, 1951.

[3] C. F. von Weizsäcker, *The World View of Physics*, U. of Chicago Press, 1952.

[4] Karl Barth, *Kirchliche Dogmatik*, Vol. 3-1 (for the discussion of Leibniz and his followers).

[5] A. d'Arbro, *The Rise of the New Physics*, Vol. I (Classical Physics), Dover Publ., New York, 1951.

[6] H. F. Stewart, *Blaise Pascal, Pensees*, Routledge and K. Paul, London, 1950 (this is the best English translation).

CHAPTER FOUR

Conservation Laws

In this chapter a number of rules, known as conservation laws and useful for the solution of problems in physics, will be discussed. They are the laws of conservation of energy, of linear momentum and of angular momentum. In the past exaggerated claims have been made about the philosophical and theological significance of these laws. For that reason it is important to show how these laws originated and how they are used. It can then be seen that the claims are unfounded.

In this discussion, as well as in later ones, it is important to become familiar with the concepts of scalar and vector quantities. The meaning of these concepts can be illustrated as follows. Suppose you live in a town A and want to go to town B. If somebody tells you that town B is 100 miles from town A, then this gives some information about town B (its distance to town A), but it does not pinpoint its location! Quantities that have magnitude (such as "so many miles"), but no direction, are known as *scalar* quantities. If, however, somebody tells you that town B lies 100 miles due west of town A, then this describes its location completely, since it gives distance as well as direction. Quantities that have magnitude (such as "100 miles") and direction (such as "due west") are known as *vector* quantities. Scalar quantities are measured by numbers and are added just as numbers. Vector quantities are measured by numbers *and* directions and are added differently. The latter is only a technical detail, however, that does not concern us here.

The concepts of energy and momentum in physics and in everyday life have considerable similarity. We commonly associate "energy" with the potentiality to *do* something and associate "momentum" with quantity of motion. These associations are also valid in physics. The difference is that physics gives quantitative answers to questions, so that we need quantitative measures for energy, linear momentum and angular momentum. This means that we have to relate these quantities to other known quantities of the system, such as mass, distance, velocity, etc. These relations, in turn, imply that we have to define the energy, linear momentum and angular momentum in mathematical forms and have to express them in terms of mass, distance, velocity, etc.

1. Energy law.

In the case of the law of conservation of energy a certain quantity, the energy, is defined for a physical process in such a manner that its total amount remains constant during the process. If no energy is supplied to the system from the outside, then the energy law states that the energy of the system remains constant. If energy *is* supplied to the system, then the energy law states that the change in energy equals the energy supplied.

There are many forms of energy. If a new phenomenon is encountered, one often has to introduce a new form of energy to make the energy law hold. We shall illustrate this with the help of examples.

One form of energy is *mechanical work*. If a force F moves a body of mass m over a distance s, then the *mechanical work* W is defined as $W = Fs$. According to Newton's second law the force F produces an acceleration $a = F/m$, and as a consequence the body will have obtained a velocity v at the end of its path. A calculation shows that if the body was initially at rest, then the velocity v is such that the relation:

$$Fs = \tfrac{1}{2}mv^2 \qquad\qquad (1)$$

holds. If the *kinetic energy* T of the body, or its "energy of motion," is now defined as $T = \tfrac{1}{2}mv^2$, equation (1) reads: *"The mechanical work done by the force equals the kinetic energy obtained by the body."* This is the law of conservation of energy for this system.

Next consider a stone of mass m that is thrown vertically upward with a velocity v_0. Because the earth is attracting the stone with a force F that is proportional to its mass m, we may write $F = mg$, where $g = F/m$ is the downward acceleration of the body caused by this attraction. As a consequence, the velocity v of the stone decreases when the stone moves upward, becomes zero when the stone reaches its maximum height, and then its magnitude increases when the stone goes down. If one calculates the velocity v at a distance h above the ground, one obtains the relation:

$$\tfrac{1}{2}mv^2_0 = \tfrac{1}{2}\,mv^2 + mgh \qquad\qquad (2)$$

If now the quantity mgh is introduced as the *potential energy*,* or as the "energy of location," of the stone with respect to ground, then this equation states: *During the motion of the*

---

*The potential energy mgh represents the mechanical work done *against* the gravitational force mg.

stone the sum of kinetic and potential energy remains constant. This is again the law of conservation of energy.

If one drives a car, energy has to be supplied by the gasoline to keep the car moving. What happens to this energy? It is used to overcome friction. Thus, the energy law states in this case: *The energy supplied equals the mechanical work done against the frictional forces.* What, in turn, happens to this mechanical work? It re-appears as heat, raising the temperature of the bearings, the tires, the road, etc.

Heat is thus another form of energy. It took quite an effort before this insight was gained during the last century. Presently everybody is familiar with the molecular structure of matter and it no longer seems unreasonable that heating a body results in an increase in the average energy of individual molecules and that the absolute temperature* T of the body is a measure for this average energy. As a matter of fact, the kinetic theory of heat shows that the average energy of the molecules is proportional to T. The total energy of the molecules is known as the *internal energy*.

As a next example, consider a vertical cylinder of gas closed by a piston carrying a weight W on top. If the cylinder is heated, the gas expands. In this case the internal energy of the gas is increased and mechanical work is done against the opposing force W. The energy law now reads: *"The heat supplied equals the increase in internal energy plus the work done against the external force."*

This form of the energy law is known as the *first law of thermodynamics*. It implies that a machine can only perform

---

*Absolute temperature means that the zero point of the temperature scale is at *absolute zero*, that is, at the temperature at which the average energy of the molecules is zero; this temperature is at —273.16° C.

mechanical work if the necessary energy is supplied. It can also be put in the form: "A machine that would perform more mechanical work than would correspond to the energy supplied is impossible." A machine that would perform such a function is known as a *perpetual motion machine of the first kind*. It is interesting to note that inventors still try to patent machines that violate this principle. Usually they feel persecuted when the patent bureau does not grant their patent.

These examples are sufficient to show the general pattern followed in developing the energy law. Time and again the energy law known in the form that it had at that moment was found to be violated. There are then two ways out of such a difficulty:

a) One could state how much energy appears or disappears under the given conditions.

b) One could introduce a new form of energy so that the energy law becomes valid again.

It is obvious that these two alternatives are formally equivalent so that it does not make any difference which of these two ways is chosen. It is, however, much more *convenient* to choose the second way. For that reason physicists uphold the law of conservation of energy. Occasionally we will thus come back to this law and introduce new forms of energy such as: electrical energy, radiant energy, energy associated with mass, etc.

2. The laws of conservation of momentum.

The linear momentum p of a body of mass m and velocity v is defined by the relation:

$$p = mv \qquad (3)$$

It may be shown from Newton's laws of mechanics that the total linear momentum* of a system remains constant if no external force is acting upon the system. If external forces are acting, the change in linear momentum corresponds to the momentum supplied by the external forces. This law is known as the *law of conservation of linear momentum*. It is of great importance in collision problems.

Just as a body is set into rectilinear motion if acted upon by a force of constant direction so a body is set into pure rotation by applying a *torque*, that is, a set of two equal and opposite forces not acting along the same line. Whereas the rectilinear motion of a body is described by its linear momentum p, so the rotary motion of a body is described by its angular momentum J. The *angular momentum J* of a body of mass m rotating in a circle of radius r with a speed v is defined as:**

$$J = mvr \qquad (4)$$

It may be shown from Newton's laws of mechanics that in any system upon which no external torques are working, the angular momentum does not change. If an external torque is acting, the change in angular momentum corresponds to the angular momentum supplied by the torque. This is the *law of conservation of angular momentum*. It is the basis for the operation of the gyroscope.

As long as one stays in the realm of mechanics, the two conservation laws of momentum follow directly from the equations. If one goes outside that field, however, one finds time and

---

*The momentum p of a body is a *vector*, since it has magnitude and direction. The total momentum of the system is equal to the sum of the momenta of its individual parts.

**The angular momentum is a vector. It has magnitude and direction. Because rotation always proceeds along an *axis*, the direction of the angular momentum vector is defined as the direction of its axis of rotation.

again that these laws are violated. To uphold the conservation laws one then must introduce new forms of momentum and new means of supplying or carrying away momentum. For example, radiation has linear and angular momentum associated with it. To uphold the conservation laws in some nuclear transmutations one had to postulate the existence of practically undetectable particles, the neutrinos. (Chapter 10.) The situation here is thus similar to the one found for the energy law.

3. Consequences of the conservation laws[1,2].

I am of the opinion that the laws of conservation of energy and momentum are imposed upon nature by man. I am careful not to expand this into the statement that *all natural laws are imposed upon nature by man.* On the other hand, I am also unwilling to go along with the opposite statement that *all natural laws are imposed upon man by nature.* The reason is that the truth lies somewhere in between these two extremes: *we* impose some laws upon nature and *nature* imposes some laws upon us. As indicated previously, it is clear to my mind that *we* impose the energy law and the momentum laws. On the other hand, the structure of the atom and of the atomic nucleus are forced upon us by the experimental evidence; we do not impose them upon nature.

My point of view is in contrast with the one voiced by such eminent physicists as Max Planck and (to a lesser extent) von Weizsäcker. According to Max Planck, the energy law is one of the most clear-cut cases of a law that nature imposes upon us. He contrasts his point of view with that one of those physicists, whom he labels "positivists," who maintain that *all* laws of nature are imposed upon nature by the scientists themselves. The author does not agree with that extreme point of view, but is of the opinion that the energy law should not be quoted against it. Von Weizäcker is much more careful but his views tend to go in a similar direction as Max Planck's.

Max Planck's reasons for his point of view were of a religious nature. According to him, the conservation laws were an indication of the existence of God. I cannot go along with this. Though I am in favor of defending religion, I am opposed against defending it with *wrong* arguments. And an argument based on the conservation laws is not a good one. A theology that starts from science has up to now ended up in humanism and not in Christianity. Leibniz and his followers and Planck, but not von Weizsäcker, give good examples of it.

This should not surprise us at all. If the basic concepts of Christianity are independent of science, and I think they are, then they can only get into our system of thinking by *putting* them in explicitly. One can put it in this way: "What you do not put in first, you cannot get out later." This rule holds, of course, for a much wider area than physics alone.

What then is the scope of the conservation laws? They differ from laws like the law of gravitation or the laws governing the structure of the atom, which are more or less statements of fact. They are primarily powerful methods for organizing our knowledge and our understanding of natural phenomena. It is always a sensible question to ask: "What happens to the energy and to the linear and the angular momentum?" Having obtained the answer to this question often brings a difficult problem closer to its solution.

We may put it as follows: "The conservation laws prescribe to us some of the questions that we should ask nature." We might also say: "The conservation laws are not laws of nature but dogmas of natural science." This happens to fit with what Herman Diem[3] says about the relation between the dogmas and the Holy Scriptures in Christian theology: "Es wird uns nicht vorgeschrieben was die Texte sagen müssen, sondern nur woraufhin wir sie zu befragen haben."* This is only an analogy of *method,* of course; the content is completely different in the two cases.

---

*It is not prescribed to us what the texts have to say, but only what questions we have to ask them.

REFERENCES:

[1] Max Planck, *Scientific Biography,* Philosophical Library, 1949; *Vorträge und Erinnerungen,* S. Hirzel, Stuttgart, 1949.

[2] C. F. von Weizsäcker, *History of Nature,* Univ. of Chicago Press, 1949.

[3] H. Diem, *Theologie II,* Kaiser Verlag, München, 1955.

CHAPTER FIVE

Thermodynamics
Statistical Mechanics

In this chapter the second law of thermodynamics and its consequences are discussed. The first law of thermodynamics deals with the *quantity* of energy, whereas the second law deals with its *quality*. For example, a certain amount of energy in a heat reservoir at a high temperature is more useful than the same amount of energy in a heat reservoir at a low temperature, since the first reservoir can be used to run an engine whereas the second can not.

The second law of thermodynamics states that energy has a tendency to *degrade,* that is, to go from a more useful to a less useful form. This allows us to predict the direction in which a great number of physical, chemical and biological processes go. To facilitate the discussion, concepts such as the *entropy* or "reduced heat" concept, which is a measure for the quality of the energy available in the system under discussion, are introduced.

Next, it is pointed out that the second law and its equivalents have a statistical basis. They are not absolutely valid, but gross deviations from the law are extremely unlikely. This fact opens up the possibility to connect the entropy of a system with the probability of its configuration. The discussion gives an opportunity to show how statistical considerations enter into physics and to clarify the meaning of terms such as "random phenomena" and "random processes." It leads to identifying the entropy with the "degree of randomness" of the system.

Finally, certain claims about the philosophical and theological consequences of thermodynamics are dealt with.

1. The second law of thermodynamics.

We already mentioned the first law of thermodynamics according to which the heat supplied to a system equals the sum of the increase in internal energy of the system and the work done against external forces. We saw that this ruled out the possibility of a *perpetual motion machine of the first kind,* which would perform work without having energy supplied to it. That principle would not be violated, however, if one built an engine that would simply take heat from some large reservoir (e.g. the sea) and convert it completely into useful work. Neither would it be violated if one built a refrigerator that simply conveyed heat from a cold body to a hotter one without having to do work to achieve it. Nevertheless, such desirable devices, known as *perpetual motion machines of the second kind,* do not exist. There are still inventors, however, that claim to have achieved this desirable goal. They do not understand why the patent bureau does not grant them patent rights.

The impossibility of such devices is formulated in the *second law of thermodynamics.* It occurs in two forms:

1. *Clausius' formulation.* It is impossible for a self-acting machine to convey heat continuously from one body to another at a higher temperature. This forbids the refrigerator.

2. *Kelvin's formulation.* It is impossible by means of any continuous inanimate agency to derive mechanical work from any portion of matter by cooling it below the lowest temperature of its surroundings. This forbids the engine.

One has to be careful with such generalized formulations. It is true that perpetual motion machines of the second kind have never been made. But not everything that has not been found is impossible. Otherwise there would be no new discoveries. Why, then, can one be so sure that such machines do not occur? Actually, one cannot be so sure, at least not at this stage of our investigation. At the present level the justification of the second law is that it allows to tie a large amount of physical and chemical data together, and that its predictions about new physical and chemical relationships have always been confirmed by experiments up to now. Later, after having discussed statistical mechanics, we shall see the basis of the second law as well as its limitations.

2. Reversible and irreversible processes. Entropy.

A physical process is called *reversible,* if the system undergoing the process is in equilibrium at all times. If there is no equilibrium at all times, the process is called *irreversible.* For example, consider a cylinder filled with gas and closed by a piston. If the piston is moved very slowly, one has approximately a reversible expansion or contraction of the gas, since there is approximately equilibrium at all times. But if the piston were moved suddenly, there would be no equilibrium at all times and the process would be definitely irreversible.

Any passage from a nonequilibrium to an equilibrium state is, by its very nature, irreversible. For example, a hot body put into an environment of lower temperature will ultimately cool down to the temperature of its environment. In practice, a heat engine is never operating in a fully reversible manner, for that would imply infinitely slow compression of the gas in its cylinders. A good engine may come close to this ideal, however, and therefore the concept of reversibility is a useful one.

To predict the thermodynamic behavior of a given system one introduces quantities such as entropy, free energy, enthalpy, etc. They are useful for determining equilibrium conditions and for evaluating whether certain physical or chemical processes will go off spontaneously. We illustrate this with the help of the entropy concept.

Let a certain system have an absolute temperature T and let an amount of heat ΔQ be applied to the system. The increase in the entropy of the system is then defined as $\Delta S = \Delta Q/T$. Because of this definition the entropy concept is also known as the "reduced heat" concept; it measures the *quality* of the energy content of the system.

For larger steps involving a total amount Q of applied heat the temperature changes. One then splits Q into small steps ΔQ and takes the sum over all amounts ΔS ($= \Delta Q/T$). By defining a zero point for the entropy one has introduced a complete entropy scale.

To illustrate the use of the entropy concept, let us investigate processes in which no heat is applied from an external source. Such processes are known as *adiabatic* processes. According to the definition of entropy, the entropy does not change if this process is carried out in a reversible manner. If the process is carried out in an irreversible manner, it may be shown that the entropy increases during the process. This leads to the following general rules:

1. In any closed system*, left to itself, the entropy will either stay constant (for reversible processes) or will increase with time (for irreversible processes).

2. Any possible change in a closed system that results in an increase in entropy will actually occur.

3. An equilibrium condition is attained if the entropy of the system has attained its maximum value.

These rules, which are fully equivalent to the second law of thermodynamics, give the basis for many equilibrium considerations in physics and chemistry. The equilibrium condition between a liquid and its vapor, the direction of chemical reactions and physical processes, etc., can be determined from it.

For example, consider a body of temperature T_1 brought into an environment of lower temperature T_2. If the hot body loses an amount of heat ΔQ to the environment, then the change in entropy of the hot body is $\Delta Q/T_1$ and the change in entropy of the environment is $\Delta Q/T_2$. The net change in entropy $(-\Delta Q/T_1 + \Delta Q/T_2)$ is thus positive. According to the second rule the cooling of the hot body goes off spontaneously, in accordance with everyday experience. This example indicates that the entropy of a *part* of a closed system may decrease in a spontaneous process. The *total* entropy of the closed system will always increase, however.

For the above reason it has often been stated that the entire universe will ultimately reach a permanent state of equilibrium, the so-called "heat death," in which all available energy has been converted into heat and all bodies have come to the same (low) temperature. The validity of such a conclusion depends on the answer to questions such as: "Is the universe finite or

---

*A closed system is a system to which no heat is supplied and from which no heat is extracted.

infinite?" and: "Is the universe a closed system to which no energy is supplied in any form?" Whatever the case, there is little reason for concern. For the calamity, if it ever occurs, is many billions of years away. In between, many other calamities may happen, as will be seen in chapter 13. It is, however, an interesting topic in popular discussions on science.

Of greater importance is the following consideration. Practically all processes occur in a more or less irreversible manner, so that the entropy will always increase with time. All processes run off in such a manner that the total entropy increases. The flow of events in such a system is thus *unidirectional*. If the universe is considered to be a closed system, then the succession of events in the universe is *unique* and nonrepeatable. Von Weizsäcker has aptly called this "die Geschichlichkeit der Natur" (the historic character of nature)[1]. Others have characterized this situation by speaking of entropy as "time's arrow."[3]

3. The kinetic theory of gases. Fluctuations.

It is known from a large background of experimental data that gases consist of molecules and that the laws of mechanics hold for the motion of these molecules. But that means that the behavior of gases can be treated as a problem of mechanics and that the theory of heat can be put on a mechanical basis. Two old, but important, fields of physics have hereby been unified.

In carrying out this unification in practice, an interesting theoretical problem arises. A cubic foot of gas at atmospheric pressure contains about 10^{24} (one million billion billion) molecules. This number is so huge that one can never hope to know all the initial conditions. And to predict the future motion of the molecules one would have to know all the initial conditions extremely accurately. For the slightest error in the initial condition of even one molecule might make it uncertain whether a certain collision with another molecule will or will not take place. At first sight the theoretical problem thus seems hopeless. Actually, the presence of so many molecules simplifies the theoretical problem considerably, since it allows to apply the probability laws holding for systems that contain large numbers.

To illustrate this, consider the problem of life insurance. Suppose an insurance firm has one million policyholders, each with a life insurance policy of $10,000. If all policyholders died simultaneously, the company would go bankrupt. However, that is such an extremely unlikely event that one does not have to consider it. One does not even have to know which policyholder is going to die when. All that is needed is to know that the group of policyholders is sufficiently large, for in that case one can be sure that each cause of a short life and each cause of a long life will be present in the proper proportion. In addition, one can reduce the risk to the company by giving the applicants a physical checkup before the insurance deal is closed. Taking all the risks involved into account, one can determine the premium payments needed to have the company make money. The continuing prosperity of the life insurance firms indicates the feasibility of this procedure.

The same is true in gases. Here most of the quantities of interest are *average* quantities. For example, in problems involving volumes of gas, one wants to know the average gas pressure, that is, the average force exerted upon the wall by the moving molecules colliding with it. All that is needed to know is the average number of molecules colliding with the wall per second and the average momentum transferred to the wall by the individual molecules. It is unnecessary to know *when* an individual molecule collides with the wall. Also, it is often important to know the internal energy of the gas. It is found by multiplying the number of molecules with the average energy per molecule. It is unnecessary to know the energy of *each* individual molecule.

This brings us to the problem of *spontaneous fluctuations*. To illustrate how these come about, we turn to the pressure of a gas. The number of molecules colliding with a unit wall area per second is huge. Its number is not constant, however, but fluctuates. As a consequence, the total force exerted upon the wall by these collisions is not constant either. Because of the huge number of molecules involved, the fluctuations in the force exerted upon the wall are quite small, and it takes very accurate measurements to observe them. With the help of a sensitive microphone these pressure fluctuations can be transformed into electrical signals that can be amplified with an electronic amplifier. The amplified signal may then be fed into a loudspeaker and made audible as a hissing sound (noise) or fed into indicating instruments and be measured.

To the observer these spontaneous pressure fluctuations are *random*. He cannot account for the exact deviation from the mean pressure value at a given time, since he cannot observe at the *microscopic level*. If he could, he would see the collisions of the individual molecules with the wall and the fluctuations would thereby find their causal explanation. Since he can only observe at the macroscopic level, he cannot see the causes of the fluctuations and hence they appear to him as random.

The occurrence of random phenomena indicates that one is operating at a level of investigation that is disturbed by phenomena occurring at a deeper lying level. In such a case the theory cannot make a full prediction of the observations. It can only give the *probability* that a certain result will be found experimentally. Repeating the measurement a large number of times allows to determine this probability experimentally[2].

The second law of thermodynamics gives a description of the phenomena at the *macroscopic* level. It does not deal with microscopic fluctuations around the equilibrium conditions themselves or around the paths along which these equilibrium conditions are reached. Small violations of the second law of thermodynamics occur frequently, but significant violations are so rare that they can be ignored for all practical purposes. To understand that, the role of probability in thermodynamics has to be discussed in greater detail.

4. Probability and entropy[1].

Let us consider a die having the numbers 1 to 6 written on its six sides. If the die is properly constructed and properly thrown, all six sides have equal likelihood of turning up. The probability of throwing 3 in a given throw is thus $1/6$, since there are six possible numbers that can come up and only one of them actually occurs in a single throw. What is the probability that two throws yield the combination 6-6? There are now $6 \times 6 = 36$ possible combinations (3-5, 5-3, 4-2, 6-6 etc.) and only one of them gives us the wanted combination, hence the probability is $1/36$. In the same way the probability of throwing three sixes in a row is $1/216$, since there are $6 \times 6 \times 6 = 216$ possible combinations and only one of them corresponds to 6-6-6. The probability of a given sequence of successive events is thus equal to the *product* of the probabilities of the individual events. This is an important rule that we have to remember.

Let us apply this to the case of a volume V of gas containing N molecules. Suppose at the time $t = 0$, all these molecules were located in a small volume element v. What is the probability that such an event happened spontaneously, if each position in the volume V is equally likely? The chance of a single molecule being in the volume v is then v/V, and the chance that all N molecules are in the small volume v is $(v/V)^N$. In view of the fact that N is so extremely large, this condition is so improbable that one would practically never encounter it.

What one finds instead, is that the N molecules are distributed practically evenly through the volume V. The expected *average* number of molecules in the volume v is thus $(v/V)N$. The number of particles in the volume v will fluctuate around this equilibrium value, but these fluctuations are quite small and go unnoticed unless one looks for them with the help of sensitive methods.

The situation is quite different, of course, if the N molecules were *released* in the small volume element v at the time $t = 0$. In that case the molecules will spread out rapidly and in a very short time they will be practically evenly distributed in space. A system having a large number of particles, left to itself, will thus tend to go from a less probable state to a more probable state until the most probable state is reached. After that it will show small fluctuations around that state.

We saw before, that a system, left to itself, would tend to go from a state of lower entropy to a state of higher entropy, until the state of maximum entropy is reached. Thus, there seems to be a relation between entropy and probability. This actually is the case; the entropy of a system may be defined as being proportional to the logarithm of the probability of the state in which the system is in. It may be shown that this definition is equivalent to the previous one.*

---

*The new definition of entropy reflects the fact that entropies are additive, whereas probabilities are multiplied. Since the logarithm of the product of two terms equals the sum of the logarithms, the definition is a sensible one.

The laws concerning the entropy and the second law of thermodynamics are thereby put on a statistical basis. They do not hold with *absolute* certainty but their probability is so close to unity that notable exceptions can be neglected in practical cases.

If a system is in a nonequilibrium state at the instant $t = 0$, the future behavior of the system can be predicted. Can past behavior also be predicted? It turns out that it cannot. If one tries to predict the past, using the existing probability laws, one obtains a curious result. It is found that the system, left to itself, must have come from a state of larger probability to its present state of smaller probability, just the opposite of what was predicted for the future. The reason for this peculiar conclusion lies in the seemingly innocent expression "left to itself." It implies that the improbable state at the instant $t = 0$ *occurred accidentally as a very improbable large spontaneous fluctuation.*

Let us illustrate this with our previous example. If, at a certain instant, all N molecules happened to be in the small volume v by chance, then they must have come from other parts of the large volume V. If one had looked slightly earlier, one would have found that some of the molecules were not yet in the volume v. Still earlier, many more molecules would not yet have been in that volume. Long before that instant, the number of molecules in the small volume v would have been very close to the average value. Any theory that involves statistical considerations *can thus predict the probable course of events for the future, but not the probable course of events for the past.* In one way or the other these considerations always enter in.

One can also look at this from another point of view. If one comes across a very improbable situation that is tending toward a more probable condition, *then one can be reasonably sure that this improbable situation was set in the past.* For if the situation is very unlikely, it is very improbable that it could have occurred spontaneously. Suppose one night you enter through your front door, smell no gas in the hall, some gas in the living room, more in the dining room, and you notice the strongest smell in the kitchen, then you can be quite sure that somebody must have turned on a burner of the kitchen gas stove while the pilot light was not burning. From the distribution of the gas through the house it would even be possible to estimate how long ago the gas was turned on.

This reasoning has been used in favor of creation as follows. If the universe is now in an improbable state and if it was in a still more improbable state in the past, then an initial even more improbable condition must have been *set* in the (distant) past. As will be seen in our discussion of the expanding universe, it is a plausible possibility. To consider it as a firm foundation on which to build one's faith in a Creator, is quite a different matter. Moreover, it would not lead to the Creator of which the Christian message speaks, but to a Creator who retired after having set the initial conditions and having switched on the machinery of the universe. The reasoning is thus of rather doubtful value.

5. Entropy as a measure of the degree of randomness[3].

Consider as an example an amount of gas to which a given amount of energy has been supplied. First assume that all molecules have the same energy. This is a very unlikely situation, since it can only occur in *one* manner. Next consider the case that the molecules have different energies. At a particular instant let N_1 *have an energy* E_1, N_2 an energy E_2, . . . etc. Since it is not asked *which* molecules have that energy, there are a large number of different situations which lead to the same distribution N_1, N_2, . . . Such a condition is thus much more probable than the previous one. If initially all molecules had the same energy, the energy distribution of the individual molecules at a later date would be randomly distributed in time because of the many mutual collisions. Instead of stating that a system left to itself will tend toward the most probable condition, one may also say that it will tend toward the condition with the greatest degree of randomness. Entropy may thus be considered as a measure for the degree of randomness.

To illustrate this point further, consider a sample of solid material in an evacuated container whose walls can stand high temperatures. The atoms in the solid are strongly bound to equilibrium positions and vibrate around it with amplitudes that increase with increasing temperature. If heat is supplied to the solid, the individual atoms will start to vibrate more strongly, so that the degree of randomness of their configuration increases. This is accompanied by an increase in entropy.

At a certain temperature the solid melts. The molecules are now no longer bound to equilibrium conditions but can move through the molten material, so that their degree of randomness has increased greatly. A large amount of heat must be supplied to do the melting and this corresponds to a considerable increase in entropy. Again, the degree of randomness and the entropy increase in the same direction.

At a still higher temperature the liquid starts to boil. If the temperature is raised high enough all the liquid will be transformed into vapor. The molecules can now move through the whole container, so that their degree of randomness has again increased strongly. A large amount of heat has to be supplied to do the evaporation and this corresponds to a large increase in the entropy of the system.

Next consider the case that the solid is cooled instead of heated. The lower the temperature, the smaller the vibrations of the atoms and hence the smaller their degree of randomness. Cooling the system corresponds to decreasing its entropy, so that the degree of randomness and the entropy change again in the same direction.

These considerations can be applied to living systems. A living animal is a very unlikely configuration of molecules. Left to itself it would tend to the much more probable condition of decay and distintegration. As a matter of fact, it does just that when it is dead. It can only maintain this improbable configuration, and even make it more improbable by growing, if there is an intake of energy in the form of food. In the same manner one can conclude that biological evolution, if and when it occurs, is only possible as long as energy is supplied to the biological systems.

6. Conclusions.

Whenever a new concept comes up, sweeping and unjustified generalizations are often made. The introduction of statistical considerations was no exception. The use of statistics in crime studies implies that one can ignore whether any particular individual is a law-abiding citizen or whether he has criminal tendencies. In a sufficiently large sample one has enough of each group to make the predicted average come out reasonably accurate. It would be completely wrong to claim: "The use of statistics implies that there are no law-abiding citizens and that everybody has an equal chance of committing a crime," as seems to have been said by some social scientists of the 19th century.

We saw that the use of differential equations did not imply determinism and that the use of variational principles does not indicate that the universe is built on teleological principles. In the same manner the use of statistics does not imply indeterminism and the occurrence of random phenomena does not mean that we live in a universe where everything is ruled by chance.

It has also been argued that the statistical considerations open up the possibility for the occurrence of miracles. There are no impossible events, but only likely, less likely and extremely unlikely events. It is thus possible, though very unlikely, that something occurs that goes against the existing order and against common experience. But this means that "miracles" can and even "must" occur if one waits long enough.

In these considerations miracles are defined as events that go against the existing order of things. That is a somewhat unfortunate definition, as will be seen later. What is even more unfortunate is that in this point of view miracles occur "by the grace of statistics," whereas the Christian point of view is that they occur "by the grace of God." In my opinion this is a long step backwards that does not solve anything and only creates confusion.

All the principles, concepts and methods of the natural sciences have their proper place. But one should be careful not to extend them beyond their limits and draw irresponsible conclusions from them.

REFERENCES:

[1] C. F. von Weizsäcker, *History of Nature*, l.c.

[2] D. Bohm, *Causality and Chance in Modern Physics*, l.c.

[3] H. F. Blum, *Time's Arrow and Evolution*, Princeton Univ. Press, 1951. (Applies thermodynamics to the life sciences.)

CHAPTER SIX

Electromagnetism and Light

The development of mechanics was greatly helped by the fact that most of its concepts can be visualized. It is not so difficult to grasp the meaning of the concepts of force, velocity, acceleration and mass. When one enters the realm of electromagnetic phenomena this is no longer the case. It is difficult to visualize magnetic poles, electric charges, electric and magnetic fields. To remedy it, considerable time was spent in the 19th century to develop mechanical models of electric and magnetic phenomena. At present this urge has subsided but one still finds relics of this distant past in textbooks on electromagnetism.

We shall now discuss the basic laws of electromagnetism. This will give us an opportunity to deal with the use and misuse of analogies in the natural sciences.

1. Static electricity. Action at a distance and field theories[1-2].

It was found many centuries ago that amber and glass, after having been rubbed against fur, could attract small pieces of paper. These materials were said to become "electrically charged" when treated that way. Later it was found that the electricity caused by rubbing amber and by rubbing glass was not alike. For that reason Benjamin Franklin introduced the concepts of *positive* and *negative* electricity. The glass was said to be positively charged and the amber negatively charged. Experiments indicated that like charges repelled each other whereas unlike charges attracted each other. Furthermore, it was shown that electric charge could move readily in some materials and not at all in others. The first materials were called *conductors* of electricity and the second became known as *non-conductors* or *insulators*. Positive and negative charges could neutralize each other. If a conductor was first charged positively and then the proper amount of negative charge was added, the electric effects were found to disappear.

All this is not so surprising at present, for we know that a neutral atom consists of a positively charged nucleus surrounded by negatively charged electrons moving around the nucleus and more or less strongly bound to it. Charging a body positively means *removing electrons;* charging it negatively means *adding electrons.* Electrons can move freely in conductors but they cannot move in insulators. The atomic theory of electricity does not explain *why* there are positively charged nuclei and negatively charged electrons, but it merely interprets the phenomena in terms of these charges.

Coulomb put the law of attraction and repulsion between charges in a quantitative form by formulating what is now known as Coulomb's law. This law states that the force F between two charges q_1 and q_2 acts along the line joining the charges, and that its magnitude is proportional to both q_1 and

q_2 and inversely proportional to the square of the distance r between the charges:

$$F = fq_1q_2/r^2 \qquad (1)$$

where f is a proportionality factor. By choosing a particular value for f one thereby defines the unit of charge.

Coulomb's law shows a complete formal analogy with Newton's law of gravitational attraction. This was no accident. Around 1800 the scientists held Newton's law in so great esteem that they patterned new laws after it. The objection that Coulomb had no choice, since this was the law as he found it, is only partly valid. Coulomb's formulation of the laws of electrostatics is built upon the analogy between electrical attraction and gravitational attraction. If he had started from another, now prevalent, analogy, he would have formulated the laws of electrostatics in a completely different manner. Though it can be shown mathematically that the two formulations are fully equivalent, a layman would have trouble in seeing this equivalence. In the earlier days even the scientists had trouble with it.

The analogy just referred to started with introducing the concept of *field*. To handle more complex situations it was necessary to represent Coulomb's law by a differential equation. To that end one had to introduce two new quantities: the electric field strength and the electric potential. The names of Faraday and Maxwell are associated with these developments.

The electric field strength E in a certain point P represents the force on a unit test charge brought to that point. It has magnitude and direction; it is thus a *vector* quantity. The electrostatic potential V in a certain point P represents the work that must be done to bring a unit test charge from infinity to the point P. It has magnitude only; it is thus a *scalar* quantity.

By these definitions a vector and a scalar quantity are assigned to every point in space. One speaks of a *vector field* if a vector quantity is assigned to every point in space and of a *scalar field* if a scalar quantity is assigned to every point in space. The meaning of these "fields" can be visualized by means of the following examples. Contour maps of a mountainous country help to visualize a scalar field, since a scalar quantity, the height, is assigned to all points on the map. The flow of liquid from a faucet over nearly level ground can help to visualize a vector field, since a vector quantity, the flow velocity, can be assigned to every point on the ground.

It should be emphasized that these fields are introduced in a formal manner, and that they do not imply that something "happened" to space. This was quickly forgotten, however. The formal concepts soon became filled with physical meaning. In some cases this helped the understanding of electric phenomena and in other cases it hampered it.

To deal with fields one has to apply a branch of mathematics known as vector calculus. Unfortunately that branch of mathematics was not well developed in the early 19th century. Moreover, Faraday had received little formal training in mathematics and thus had to operate with more or less picture-like mechanical concepts.* For example, he pictured electricity as an electric fluid with the following properties:

1) The fluid is incompressible and fills the universe.

2) In conductors the fluid can move freely. In insulators and free space its molecules are bound to equilibrium positions.

---

*This is not said to belittle Faraday's stature as a scientist but to emphasize it. That a man with so little mathematical background could play such an important part in the development of electromagnetism is a clear indication of his genius.

3) If a conductor is positively charged, a certain amount of fluid has passed through its surface outward. If it is negatively charged, a certain amount of fluid has passed through its surface inward.

4) This motion of the fluid sets up pressure in the fluid. The displacement of the fluid is a measure for the electric field strength.

5) Displacement of the fluid in conductors, insulators and free space constitutes an electric current.

By introducing this analogy, the attention is shifted from the forces between distant charges to the action of the liquid medium or substrate on the other charges. The first is called "action at a distance" (or far-action) and the second "action through a medium" (or near-action). Let us contrast these two points of view. Suppose an isolated conducting sphere is charged by bringing small amounts of charge from the earth to the sphere. In order to do so, one has to do work. The larger the charge that is already *on* the body, the larger the amount of work that must be done to bring the next speck of charge to the sphere. There is thus "electric energy" associated with the charged sphere. In the "action at a distance" approach this electric energy is the potential energy (energy of location) of the charge. In the "action through a medium" approach the energy is located in the electric fluid itself; since all molecules of the electric fluid in the region around the sphere have been moved from their equilibrium positions, the potential energy is the energy of the displaced molecules.

The two methods of approach thus look at first sight completely different. They had, however, the same starting point and, as a consequence, they give the same final result. Unfortunately, the two methods of approach were not used to *com-*

plement each other. This would have been very valuable, since sometimes the one method of approach is more convenient and sometimes the other. They were often used to contrast each other, and two antagonistic schools of thinking developed. This shows how dangerous analogies become if the analogy is taken for a physical reality.

The concept of "action through a medium" is not bound to Faraday's electric fluid, but is associated with the fact that the electric field strength is introduced as the *fundamental* physical quantity. Any theory that treats the electric field strength in that manner is a "near-action" theory. In the opinion of the author the electric field strength is *not* a fundamental physical quantity. It plays the part of a very convenient auxiliary quantity that simplifies the mathematical formulation of the theory.

Maxwell developed the theory of electromagnetism, including electrostatics, from the point of view of vector calculus. The concepts used in vector calculus were first introduced in the study of the flow of incompressible fluids. One may thus say that Maxwell used a hydrodynamic analogy of electromagnetism. In contrast to this, Faraday used a hydrostatic analogy. Since it was not always fully realized that the two analogies are different, this has resulted in some confusion in the past. The danger can be overcome by stressing the practical use of the analogies and de-emphasizing their physical importance.

2. Magnetism and its electric basis[1,2].

It was discovered many centuries ago that the iron compound magnetite (Fe_3O_4) or lodestone had the power to attract iron particles. The effect was called *magnetism* and a magnetite bar showing it was called a *magnet*. When a bar of magnetite was dipped into iron filings, the filings were found to cling mainly to the end regions. For that reason the end regions were called *poles*. It was found that there were two kinds of poles; like poles repelled each other, whereas opposite poles attracted each other. The two poles of a magnet were of opposite kind.

Coulomb found that the law of attraction between two magnetic poles was formally equivalent to the law of attraction between two electric charges. The force between two poles was inversely proportional to the square of their distance and directly proportional to the magnetic pole strengths.

The important difference with electricity is, however, that the magnetic poles cannot be isolated. Breaking a magnetic bar in two does not result in obtaining two poles but ends up in having two magnets instead of one. Hence the magnet should not be considered as consisting of two isolated "poles" but as two opposite poles belonging together. Such an assembly is called a "magnetic dipole." This fact can be most easily interpreted if the magnet is considered as an assembly of elementary magnetic dipoles oriented in the same direction. We will come back to these elementary magnets later.

The next important discovery concerning magnetism was made possible by the invention of the electric battery by Volta. Earlier machines for generating electricity could generate large potential differences between isolated conductors but had very little capacity for generating electric currents. Electric batteries allowed to generate currents that were several orders of magnitude larger. Oersted was then able to show that a current-carrying wire deflects a magnetic needle. This indicates that a loop of wire carrying an electric current acts as a magnet and that magnetic phenomena have an electric basis.

The elementary magnetic dipoles in a magnet could now

be associated with tiny currents flowing in closed loops. At present the elementary magnetic dipoles are considered as being formed by groups of atomic magnets lined up in parallel. The atomic magnets, in turn, can be accounted for by two mechanisms:

a) Negatively charged electrons rotating around the positive nucleus of an atom can be considered as tiny currents flowing in closed loops. They thus act as tiny magnets.

b) Electrons are spinning around their axis and thus act as tiny magnets.

Usually the second mechanism is the most important.

After it was understood that magnetic effects were caused by electric currents it became possible to give a new mathematical formulation of the theory. In analogy with electrostatics the concept of magnetic field strength was introduced, but instead of the electrostatic potential, describing the electric effects caused by electric charges, the so-called magnetic vector potential, describing the magnetic effects caused by electric currents, had to be introduced.* The theory allows to express the electrostatic potential in terms of the charges and the magnetic vector potential in terms of the current densities.**

3. Electromagnetism, Maxwell's equations[1-2].

After it was established that an electric current flowing in a closed wire loop produced a magnetic field, Faraday asked

---

*Charges have magnitude but no direction, they are scalar quantities. Currents, or better, current densities, have magnitude and a direction of flow, they are vector quantities. Consequently, the magnetic effects of the current are measured by a vector quantity, the magnetic vector potential, whereas the electric effects of charges are measured by a scalar quantity, the electric potential.

**The current density in a conductor is a vector quantity. Its direction is the direction of flow of the electric charge. Its magnitude is the amount of charge crossing a unit cross-section of the conductor, perpendicular to the direction of flow, per second.

himself whether a magnetic field would also produce current in a closed wire loop. He found that this was indeed the case, provided that the loop of wire moved with respect to the magnetic field. The law describing this effect is known as *Faraday's induction law*. After it was discovered how to make alternating currents and potentials, it was found that an alternating magnetic field passing through a closed loop of wire produced an alternating current in that loop. In that case it was unnecessary to move the circuit.

Current flow in conductors is possible if an electric field is applied; without an applied field the electrons taking part in the conduction process move in random direction. Since the electrons are negatively charged, they will move in a direction opposite to the applied field. That an alternating current flowed in the induction experiment indicated that an alternating field was set up in the wire. There was thus complete symmetry. An alternating field set up in the wire gives rise to an alternating current flowing through the wire, and this, in turn, causes an alternating magnetic field around the wire. An alternating magnetic field passing through the wire loop sets up an electric field in the wire as indicated by the flow of alternating current. Electric and magnetic phenomena were thus linked together as *electromagnetic* phenomena.

In the case of an electric field caused by an alternating magnetic field the electric field is not *caused* by the wire. The conducting wire is not necessary for the *generation* of the electric field but is merely a convenient means of verifying its existence. Was the wire needed when an alternating magnetic field was set up by an alternating electric field? The answer was again "no." The concept of Faraday's electric fluid helped in arriving at this conclusion. For according to property (4) of the electric fluid, an alternating electric field set up in a vacuum corresponds to an alternating displacement of the fluid. According to property (5) this was equivalent to an electric current, the so-called "displacement current." This current was supposed to produce the same magnetic effects as an alternating current flowing through the wire.

The laws of electromagnetism could now be completely formulated. There are four major laws that were first formulated by Maxwell and bear his name. They are respectively:

a) The law relating the electric field strength and the electric charges.

b) The law relating the magnetic field strength to the fact that there are no free magnetic poles (only dipoles).

c) The law relating the magnetic field to the currents producing it.

d) The law relating a changing magnetic field to the electric field caused by it.

These four Maxwell equations are the starting point of all theoretical investigations in electromagnetism. The theoretical predictions obtained from it have always been verified by experiment. One of the most interesting results obtained by Maxwell was that he was able to show that transverse electromagnetic waves were possible.* These waves would propagate with the velocity of light. The experimental discovery of these waves in the laboratory by Hertz in 1888 verified these predictions. Our present radio communication and radar systems are based upon this discovery.

The electromagnetic waves were transverse waves propagating with the velocity of light. Since light waves showed

---

Transverse means that the alternating electric field strength and the alternating magnetic field strength are vectors directed at right angles with respect to each other and at right angles with respect to the direction of propagation of the wave.

similar properties, the proposition was made that light waves are a form of electromagnetic waves characterized by a very short wavelength. Soon the electromagnetic theory of light was adopted, long before the existence of electromagnetic waves was proved by Hertz. A great theoretical success had been achieved: the theories of electromagnetism and of light had been unified.

It had now become clear that electromagnetic phenomena were propagated with the velocity of light. At first this seemed remarkable, for in the earlier equations like Coulomb's law, etc., the "action at a distance" was supposed to occur instantaneously. How was the finite velocity of propagation introduced? An analysis shows that the supposed instantaneous action at a distance nowhere enters into the calculations and that the wave propagation comes about because of the introduction of the displacement current. This is somewhat unfortunate, since this displacement current is the weakest logical link in the whole theory. It is worth while to investigate this problem in greater detail.

In the case of electrostatics the electric potential in a point P is found by giving an expression for the contribution of the charge in a point Q, at a distance r from P, to the potential at the point P. In the case of magnetic phenomena the magnetic vector potential in a point P is found by giving an expression for the contribution of the *current density* in the point Q, at a distance r from P, to the vector potential at the point P. But if the electromagnetic phenomena are propagated with the velocity of light c, then this procedure can be extended. One should then obtain the electric potential and the magnetic vector potential at the instant t by taking for the charge and the current density in the point Q not the value at the instant t but instead the value at the instant $(t - r/c)$. If the charges do not move and the currents do not change, this gives the old "static" expressions for the potentials back. If the charges move and the currents change, the old "static" expressions are hereby replaced by the new "dynamic" ones. The idea of "action at a distance" is thereby replaced by the idea of a "propagated action of a distance." It is interesting to note that the above dynamic expressions for the potentials were derived by Gauss and Riemann long before Maxwell developed his theory.

The same expressions for the dynamic potentials can also be obtained from Maxwell's equations. The methods of "action through a medium" and "propagated action at a distance" are thus fully equivalent and it is a waste of time and energy to play the one against the other. It is worth while, however, to derive Maxwell's equations, including the displacement current term, by starting from the dynamic expressions of the electric potential and the magnetic vector potential. From a logical point of view it is more satisfying to derive Maxwell's displacement current from the "propagated action at a distance approach," for, in contrast to Maxwell's days, the propagation of electromagnetic phenomena with the velocity of light is now a well-established fact. In most practical cases it would be definitely clumsy, however, to *use* the dynamic expressions for the two potentials. It is often simpler to apply Maxwell's equations directly.

Maxwell's theory of electromagnetism is a *macroscopic* theory. It does not take into account the atomistic character of electricity. Lorentz and others carried out the program of developing an "electron theory" of electromagnetism by applying Maxwell's macroscopic equations to the space between the individual elementary charges. At first sight that seems a rather round-about way, for in a proper atomistic theory of electromagnetism one would expect all basic electromagnetic phenomena to be derivable from the formula for the forces between two arbitrarily moving charges. It turns out that such an equation, known as the Liénard force formula, can be derived in that manner. The derivation of such a formula is mainly of theoretical interest, however.

4. The ether[1-3].

The ether was introduced originally in the theory of light. Experiments had shown that light propagation was analogous to wave propagation in that interference was possible. Light plus light can give darkness, just as two waves of an opposite phase can extinguish each other. Other experiments indicated that these light waves should be represented as *transverse waves;* that is, the direction of oscillation is perpendicular to the direction of propagation. All that this says is that light should be *represented mathematically* as a transverse wave of the form:

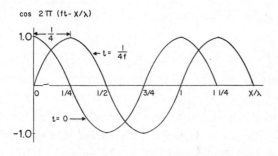

$$A \cos 2\pi \, (ft - x/\lambda) \qquad (2)$$

where A is the amplitude, f the frequency, λ the wavelength, t the time and x the distance to a fixed point of reference. Light *behaves as if* it were a transverse propagating wave, propagating with a velocity $c = f\lambda$. All that is needed in the theory is the representation of the light by an equation of the form (2). To say that light *is* a transverse propagating wave means taking an analogy for a reality. This was done in the 18th and 19th century. As a consequence the question arose whether the existence of waves postulated the existence of a medium in which these waves could propagate. The answer was affirmative, and this postulated medium was called the *ether*. In view of the transverse waves propagating in it, it was thought of as a perfect elastic solid.

Faraday's incompressible electric liquid, postulated in his theories of electromagnetism, could easily be modified into the ether. Faraday had postulated that the molecules of the liquid were bound to equilibrium positions in vacuum and in insulators. Outside a conductor the liquid thus had the properties of an elastic solid. Since it was known that the current in conductors was not carried by an electric fluid but by electrons, the "liquid flow" in conductors could be eliminated. The electric liquid and the ether were now identical. This manipulation had not changed anything to the equations. The electric fluid or solid merely illustrated the equations, but was unnecessary for their formulation.

Unfortunately, the ether turned out to have contradictory properties. Some experiments seemed to require that the earth in its motion through space did *not* carry the ether with it. One thus talked about a mysterious ether wind that passed through everything with high speed without being noticed. The ether in this point of view was considered to be at absolute rest, and therefore could serve as an *absolute* system of reference. Other experiments, such as the Michelson-Morley experiment (Chapter 7), seemed to indicate that the earth carried the ether with it. Since it seemed impossible to have an earth-convected ether on the one hand and an ether at absolute rest at the other hand, the only way out seemed to be to abandon the ether.

That this could be done was not so surprising. The ether was introduced into the theory to *illustrate* the equations of light and electromagnetism, but it did not serve any vital function in the theory. It was a superfluous embellishment of the mathematical description that could be abandoned without penalty. Eliminating the ether changed only the "window dressing" but did not alter the content of the theory. This happened after valuable scientific manpower had been wasted in the construction of complicated ether models.

5. Analogy and reality[1].

We have mentioned the word "analogy" several times. What is meant is that a certain *unknown* phenomenon is related to a *known* one. If the old problem has already been solved, the solution of the new problem is found by means of the analogy. A good analogy helps in the first place to formulate the new problem mathematically and in the second place it gives the solution.

An analogy means that a certain new phenomenon is "just as" the old one. This does not imply a physical identity but only a mathematical one. Difficulties arise if it is forgotten that the two phenomena are not *physically* identical but only have a common mathematical background. For example, the differential equations of electromagnetism are formally analogous to the equations describing the flow of noncompressible liquids. Here the analogy comes about because both phenomena can be described by *vector* fields, the electric field strength in the one case and the flow velocity field in the other. This is the *only* thing that these phenomena have in common. It is not implied that something actually "flows" in the case of electrostatic phenomena.

From a theoretical point of view all analogies that give the same final results are formally equivalent, so that it does not pay to discriminate between them. If one had to do with *realities* instead of with *analogies,* a crucial experiment could be designed that would decide between the different possibilities. Usually, however, a seemingly crucial experiment accomplishes little. After an analogy has been defeated it can often be brought back to life by modifying it and introducing new ideas into it. This is not surprising, for an analogy is mainly a *method* for transforming unknown problems back to known ones. If it does not perform this function, it has to be modified until it becomes useful once more.

In this respect somebody has made the provocative statement: "The only things that really matter are the *equations* of physics. Much of the way in which physicists talk about them is just window dressing."[1] This is, of course, an overstatement. The logical derivation of the basic equations of physics is an important task, both for educational purposes and otherwise. However, most ways of filling the analogies used in physics with physical meaning *can* be described as superfluous window dressing. Since they are superfluous, they can be abandoned at will without altering the basic content of physics. We saw that in the case of the ether.

We have here another example that should caution us not to attribute too much philosophical or theological meaning to some of the theories of physics. It is wise to look first whether one has to do with an analogy only or whether there is some physical basis behind the theory.

REFERENCES:

[1]A. O'Rahilly, *Electromagnetics*, Longmans, Green and Co., London, 1938 (highly mathematical, gives good account of the history).

[2]A. Einstein and L. Infeld, *The Evolution of Physics*, Simon and Schuster, 1942.

[3]E. Whittaker, *History of the Theories of Aether and Electricity*, London, 1951.

CHAPTER SEVEN

Relativity

The theory of relativity deals with the physics of high speed motion. It bears its name because of the theoretical method used in dealing with the problem. This method was introduced by Einstein and consists in comparing observations *relative* to moving systems of reference.

1. Special relativity[1-2-3-5].

At the same time that the optical difficulties of the ether models came to a head, it was discovered that electrons behaved strangely if their velocity came close to the velocity of light. Their mass was found to increase with increasing velocity and the interaction between moving electrons was found to depend upon their speed. The theory of electromagnetism was able to give an account of this behavior, but the results depended upon the physical "model" of the electron and there were further internal contradictions. There thus appeared to be discrepancies and inconsistencies in the mechanics and electrodynamics of high speed charged particles. Einstein succeeded in removing them in his theory of special relativity.

He was helped in this attempt by the outcome of the Michelson-Morley experiment. If the ether was at absolute rest, then the absolute velocity of the earth with respect to the ether should be observable. Michelson and Morley carried out a very accurate experiment that would enable them to detect less than 1% of the expected effect. The result was completely negative; apparently it was impossible to detect absolute motion. Einstein then developed a consistent theory based upon two postulates:

1—It is impossible, by any physical method operating within a physical system to detect a uniform motion of the system. This is known as the *principle of relativity*. It raises the negative outcome of the Michelson-Morley experiment to a basic principle of physics. It extends the experimental evidence considerably by changing the *actual* outcome of the experiment into a *necessary* one.

2—The velocity c of light in a vacuum is independent of the motion of the source or the observer. This is known as the *principle of equivalence*. It is not based on direct evidence, but with the help of it a whole body of facts can be interpreted.

Einstein was now able to prove the following results from postulates 1 and 2:

3—Equivalence of mass and energy. A mass m has an energy:

$$E = mc^2 \qquad (1)$$

and vice versa, where c is the velocity of light. This result is very important in nuclear physics and nuclear engineering. It forms the basis of atomic power developments and of the atomic bomb.

4—The mass m of a moving body increases with increasing speed v. If m_0 is the mass of the body when it is at rest (the so-called *rest mass*), then:

$$m = m_0/\surd\,(1 - v^2/c^2) \text{ and } E = m_0c^2/\surd(1-v^2/c^2) \qquad (2)$$

where E is the total energy of the moving body. The energy m_0c^2 of a particle at rest is known as the "rest energy."

5—Material particles, or particles with a rest mass m_0 that is not zero, cannot attain velocities greater than or equal to the velocity of light c.

6—Particles with zero rest mass have zero energy unless they move with the velocity of light. In the latter case the energy E is of the form o/o, which is indeterminate. We shall see in Chapter 8 that these "particles," which are known as "quanta," occur in electromagnetic radiation.

7—Quanta of energy E have a momentum $p = E/c$.

8—Quanta of energy E have a mass E/c^2.

9—Since two observers moving uniformly with respect to each other have to see *quanta as quanta,* the velocity of the quanta in a vacuum must be equal to c for all observers. This illustrates the reason why Einstein's second postulate is necessary.

Results 3-9 are a consequence of postulates 1-2, but in view of property 9 the relations between the items 1-9 can be arranged in a circle. That is, it is possible to start in another point of the circle and derive all the other results from it. For example, starting with 6 and 7 one can subsequently prove the properties 8, 3, 4, 5, 6, 9 and the postulates 2 and 1. Both methods are thus fully equivalent and as far as *results* are concerned it would be a waste of time and energy to play the one against the other.

It is not unimportant, however, as far as the pedagogical and logical aspects of the theory are concerned. The first method, originally introduced by Einstein, is based upon postulates 1 and 2. The second method starts with the experimentally established properties of the quanta and thus has a more or less phenomenological basis. In the first method the negative outcome of the Michelson-Morley experiment is the basis of the theory. In the second method the Michelson-Morley experiment is unimportant and only of historical interest. This should warn us once again not to put too much emphasis on "crucial experiments." What seems a crucial experiment in one approach to a theory may be much less important in another approach.

2. The Lorentz transformation[1-2-3-5].

In order to develop the theory of relativity for a high speed particle, Einstein had to introduce two observers, the actual observer O and a hypothetical observer O^1 co-moving with the particle. He thus had two systems of reference, each consisting of a coordinate system for measuring distances and a clock for measuring time intervals. With the help of his two postulates Einstein could transform the results observed by the observer O^1 into the results to be expected for the observer O. Since one knows the properties of a particle at rest, one can make accurate predictions about what the observer O will observe.

This transformation is known as the *Lorentz transformation*. It was introduced by Lorentz long before Einstein developed his theory, but its full significance was not understood until the theory of relativity was established. If the theory of relativity is established from the properties of quanta, then properties 3 and 4 do not have to be derived with the help of the circuitous route of the hypothetical observer co-moving with the particle, but can be proved in a straightforward manner. The Lorentz transformation is, however, an indispensable tool in most applications of the theory.

The Lorentz transformation relates coordinates and time in the reference system of the observer O to the coordinates and time in the reference system of the observer O^1. Actually, that is more than is needed. We are not interested in position and time but in *distances* and *time intervals*. This is sometimes forgotten in the discussion of the concept of *simultaneity* in the theory of relativity.

Such discussions are often found in textbooks to illustrate the revolution that the theory of relativity has brought about. Intuitively it is immediately clear what is meant with the concept of simultaneous events. Things are different, however, when two fast-moving observers look at the events. It then turns out that it cannot be established in an unambiguous manner whether or not two events occur simultaneously. Einstein had to go deeply into this problem to clarify the ideas that led to his postulates and to grasp their importance, and as such the discussion of simultaneity was helpful. Presently, however, it creates more confusion than clarification, for at its best it is a simple illustration of the Lorentz transformation and at its worst it directs the attention to the wrong problem. For in physics one is never interested in time as such, but only in time intervals that mark the duration *of* events or the duration *between* events. Physicists should therefore not become excited here. It is even more doubtful whether philosophers and theologians should become excited about the question whether absolute simultaneity can or cannot be established with certainty.

Another interesting consequence of the theory of relativity is that our everyday notion of relative velocity breaks down. If two cars travel along a road in opposite directions with speeds of 60 and 40 miles per hour, then the relative velocity of the first with respect to the second is $60 + 40 = 100$ miles, as everybody knows. But if two particles move in opposite directions with velocities v and v^1 close to the velocity of light, then the relative velocity of the first with respect to the second is still smaller than the velocity of light. This means that it cannot be equal to $(v + v^1)$. Its correct value can be determined from the Lorentz transformation.

An illustration of the Lorentz transformation that is both illuminating and of physical interest was observed in the study of cosmic rays. Primary cosmic rays are high speed nuclei coming from outer space. When they enter the top layer of the earth atmosphere, they collide with the atoms in that layer and generate a large number of high speed particles with speeds close to the velocity of light. Some of these, the mesons, are unstable particles. They decay in a very short time; at rest they have a lifetime t_0 of about 2 millionth of a second (2×10^{-6} sec.) Using that lifetime and bearing in mind that their speed is close to the velocity of light, one would expect them to travel only over several hundred yards before their decay. Actually, however, a large number of them are observed at sea level. This means that they must have traveled about 20 miles before their decay! How can this be possible?

The observer O at sea level sees particles with a speed v (close to the velocity of light c) traveling toward him. They travel the distance d between their point of origin and O. If t_0 is the lifetime measured by an observer O^1 co-moving with the particle, then the observer O will measure a lifetime t_1:

$$t_1 = t_0 / \sqrt{(1 - v^2/c^2)} \qquad (3)$$

If v is close to c, t_1 may be so much larger than t_0 that some particles can travel the distance d before they decay. What, on the other hand, does the observer O^1, moving with the particles, see? He sees particles having a lifetime t_0, but the distance d measured by the observer O looks to him like a much shorter distance d_1:

$$d_1 = d\sqrt{(1 - v^2/c^2)} \qquad (4)$$

Equations (3) and (4) follow directly from the Lorentz transformation. The effect expressed by equation (3) is known as "time dilatation" and the effect expressed by equation (4) is known as "Lorentz contraction." The reader should note again that in this example not time and position, but duration and distance are important. It is left to the imagination of the reader to speculate on the prospects that these effects open for space travel.

In the last chapter we discussed the ether, which served a double purpose. In the first place, it was the perfectly elastic medium through which light waves could propagate. In the second place, it served as the system of reference to which all measurements should be referred. The ether, as a perfectly elastic medium, was abandoned, since it had no real physical significance. The ether, as an *absolute* system of reference, is abandoned by the theory of relativity. But fixed systems of reference are there nevertheless, for the observer O refers everything back to the system of reference moving with O.

It is sometimes argued that only *relative* velocities should occur in a truly relativistic theory. If it means that they are the velocities relative to the observer O, then this is correct, for that is indeed the position taken by the theory of relativity. If "relative velocity" means the velocity of the one particle with respect to another, then this is incorrect, especially if this relative velocity is taken as the *difference* between the individual velocities observed by the observer O. It is interesting to note that such "truly relativistic theories" are still published.

The theory of relativity can be very nicely presented in a four-dimensional geometry in which the coordinates x, y, z, and ict are used. Here t is the time, c the velocity of light and $i =$

$\sqrt{(-1)}$. A mass point located at the point with coordinates (x, y, z) at the instant t is represented by a point (x, y, z, ict) in the four-dimensional space. This point is called a "world point." A point resting in space describes a straight line in this four-dimensional representation. A moving point describes a curved line in space, the so-called "world line."

This is an interesting and useful tool but it is devoid of any physical significance. We do not *live* in a four-dimensional space-time continuum, but can *represent our observations* in such a four-dimensional space-time continuum. This distinction is sometimes forgotten in popular discussions of the theory of relativity.

3. General relativity[2].

In special relativity, observations are compared in two systems of reference that are *moving uniformly* with respect to one another. In general relativity, observations are compared in two systems of reference that are *accelerated* with respect to each other. First, two simple common-sense observations.

Everybody knows from travel in elevators, that one has the feeling of being pushed "down" when the elevator accelerates in upward direction and the feeling of being pushed "up" when the elevator accelerates in downward direction. Motion in an accelerated system of reference is thus equivalent to a gravitational field acting in an opposite direction. This is known as the *principle of equivalence*.

Furthermore, it has to be noted that there are two concepts of mass. Mass occurs in the first place as a factor in Newton's law of motion $F = ma$. This quantity is called *inertial mass*. Mass occurs in the second place in the expression $F = mg$ for the force with which the earth attracts a body, where g is the acceleration that the body would obtain if it were dropped. This is called the *gravitational mass*. Since it is common sense to assume that the force on the body is the same *just before* and *just after* it has been dropped, it follows that *gravitational mass and inertial mass are equivalent*.

Up to now no new physics have been introduced. This remains true if the four-dimensional space-time continuum *(x, y, z, ict)* is used to present the observations. But now the geometry of this four-dimensional space is changed so that gravitation is automatically included into the geometry. This is achieved by giving the four-dimensional space a *curvature* at each point, depending upon its distance to the mass points present in space. A mass point moving under the influence of gravitational forces only, then becomes a mass point "left to itself." It is here that the modification of classical physical laws is introduced. Let us see how this is done.

Space as we know it, is called Euclidian space, and the geometry valid in that space is Euclidian geometry. In that geometry, space is not curved and the line of shortest distance between two points is a *straight line*. The geometry of the modified four-dimensional space is non-Euclidian, space is curved and the line of shortest distance between two points is a *curved line**. Such lines of shortest distance are known as "geodetic" lines.

The modification of classical physical laws is introduced by requiring the validity of the following basic postulate of general relativity: "A mass point left to itself, that is, with only gravitational forces acting upon it, will move along a geodetic

---

*The possibility that curved lines can be lines of shortest distance is best seen on a globe. Here the line of shortest distance between two points is a part of the great circle passing through the two points and having the center of the globe as its center.

line in the modified space-time continuum." From it the curvature of space can be determined and the theory can be developed. Unfortunately, only two effects have been discovered so far that can be considered as giving a direct confirmation of the theory.

This scanty discussion is sufficient to show that the general theory of relativity, as usually presented, is a mathematical tool used for the description of gravitational effects between fast-moving masses. These effects do not *occur* in a four-dimensional, curved, space-time continuum but are *represented* in it. It is thus possible to transform everything back into our everyday world to see what is implied physically. If that is done, one finds deviations from Newton's law for the gravitational effects between fast-moving masses*. These deviations from the gravitation law form the *real* physics introduced into the theory. It is, therefore, dangerous to ascribe too much physical significance to the framework of general relativity. It is a mathematical tool, albeit a very useful one.

The applications of general relativity to cosmology will be dealt with in a later section.

4. Unfounded conclusions from the theory of relativity[4].

It is sometimes said that relativity teaches that there are no absolutes. This is an unfounded statement. It might be argued that the theory or relativity states that there is no *preferential* system of reference for physical systems in uniform motion, though this overlooks the fact that each observer carries his own "preferred" system of reference with him. But even if this argument were conceded, that would not say anything for or against absolutes in other fields. He who decides against

---

*[1]A. O'Rahilly, l.c.

absolutes in other fields does so on his own authority and cannot claim support from relativity.

It has also been claimed that relativity has dealt a decisive blow against materialism. The argument goes that matter is "materialistic" and that energy is much more "spiritual." This has no support from the theory of relativity, for this theory claims the *equivalence* of mass and energy. Since the two points of view are equivalent, it is not allowed to play the one against the other.

It is sometimes claimed that the theory of relativity has revolutionized our concepts of space and time. The theory of relativity relates the observations made by an observer O to the observations made by an observer O^1 moving with respect to O. It does not say anything about space and time itself.

It is sometimes stated that physical measurements are carried out in a four-dimensional space-time continuum. This is not true. Physicists *do* their measurements *in the laboratory.* They can *represent* their data in a four-dimensional space-time continuum if they so wish. The four-dimensional space-time continuum has no further *physical* significance and for that reason philosophers and theologians do wise not to put too much stock in it.

REFERENCES:

[1] L. Barnett, *The Universe and Dr. Einstein,* Mentor Books, New York, 1952.

[2] A. Einstein, *Relativity, the Special and General Theory,* Henry Holt & Co., 1924.

[3] A. Einstein, *The Meaning of Relativity,* Princeton, 1946.

[4] G. Henneman, *Philosophie, Religion, Moderne Naturwissenschaft,* Luther Verlag, Witten, Germany, 1955.

[5] E. Cassirer, *Substance and Function and Einstein's Theory of Relativity,* Dover Publications (Reissue of 1923 edition).

CHAPTER EIGHT

The Older Quantum Theory

In the early 20th century it gradually became apparent that the laws of classical physics that held so well for macroscopic systems did not hold in the atomic domain. In addition, clear indications were obtained that light did not always appear as a wave phenomenon, but that it was emitted and absorbed as small packets of energy, the so-called *quanta*. Soon these new ideas were used to unravel the secrets of the atomic structure, long before wave mechanics, a consistent theory for the atomic and subatomic domain, was developed. This chapter deals with the early history of atomic physics, whereas Chapter 9 tells of the development of wave mechanics.

1. Beginning of the theory of the atomic structure[1-2].

Between 1890 and 1900 many physicists believed that physics was, to a large extent, known already. Here and there one could perhaps determine the value of a physical constant more accurately, but little new was expected. Then a whole new field, atomic physics, opened up and soon physics was in turmoil once more.

The study of conduction of electricity through gases made the earliest contribution. It was found that gases at low pressure would conduct electricity if a sufficiently large voltage was applied and that light was emitted in the process. The current was found to be carried by two types of carriers, positively charged particles (positive ions) with masses corresponding to the masses of the atoms present in the gas discharge tube and negatively charged particles, electrons, with masses about 2000 times smaller than that of the lightest positive ion (the hydrogen ion). The light emission observed depended on the gas. Since it turned out that the emitted light was a characteristic of the atoms emitting it, light emission from gas discharges became an important tool in the study of the atom.

Another interesting discovery was made in 1895 by Röntgen. He bombarded metal electrodes with high speed electrons and observed penetrating radiation, which he called X-rays. Soon it was found that these rays were electromagnetic waves of extremely short wave length. It was also observed that there were two types of X-rays: *characteristic* X-rays and *continuous* X-rays. The first had discrete wavelengths that were characteristic for the bombarded atoms. The continuous X-rays had a continuous distribution in wavelength, independent of the target material.

The electromagnetic theory of light could give a qualitative account of the light emission. According to this theory any decelerated or accelerated charged particle should emit radiation. An electron suddenly stopped in its track would emit a burst of radiation containing a whole distribution of frequencies so that this "model" could explain the continuous X-rays. An electron vibrating or rotating around an equilibrium position with a frequency f would emit light of that frequency. Unfortunately, none of the proposed "atomic models" could account for all the observed characteristic light and X-ray spectral lines.

Another clue about the structure of the atom came from the discovery of radioactivity. It was found that certain chemical elements such as Uranium and Thorium were spontaneous emitters of various forms of radiation first called α-, β- and γ-rays. The α-rays were found to consist of positively charged helium atoms, the β-rays turned out to be high speed electrons, and the γ-rays were identified as electromagnetic radiation with a wavelength even shorter than X-rays. The high energies with which these particles were emitted, gave the first inkling of the enormous amount of energy available inside the atom.

The α-particles provided a useful tool for probing the structure of the atoms. Rutherford found in that manner that the positive charge of an atom spreads over a very small area, less than 10^{-12} cm in diameter and that practically all the mass of the atom is concentrated in that area. Since an atom itself has a diameter of about 10^{-8} cm, one was forced to accept an atomic model, consisting of a positively charged nucleus, surrounded by a number of electrons.

Since all electrons were found to have the same negative charge -e, and the number of electrons in a neutral atom had to be integer, one had to assume that the positive charge on the nucleus of a neutral atom had to be Ze where Z was the number of electrons surrounding the nucleus. The question was now: "How large was Z?" A Dutch lawyer, van den Broek, suggested in 1913 that the number Z of an atom of a given element corresponded to the number that the element had in Mendeleyeff's periodic table of elements. This turned out to be correct. It is perhaps one of the last cases in which a layman made a significant contribution to physics.

Since the nucleus is so small and the atoms have a diameter of about 10^{-8} cm, one had to assume that the electrons move around the nucleus in stable orbits of about that diameter. But according to electromagnetic theory, an electron rotating around the nucleus should emit radiation and thus lose energy. The electron should therefore spiral inward toward the nucleus, and the atom would not be stable. Since atoms apparently are stable, it seemed that the laws of electromagnetic radiation did not hold here.

Another violation of a principle of classical physics turned up in the study of black body radiation. A black body is a body that absorbs all the incoming radiation. According to thermo-dynamics, all black body radiators kept at the same temperature emit the same amount of (heat) radiation per unit area. Around 1900 the spectrum of this radiation was measured carefully, and Planck succeeded in explaining the results obtained. To do so, however, he had to postulate that the elementary "harmonic oscillators" emitting and absorbing the radiation* could only have energies $E = nhf$, where f is the frequency of the oscillation, n an integral number and h a universal constant, now known as Planck's constant. This seemed to be a *necessary* postulate, for if it was assumed that the energy of the oscillators could have *all* values, as expected from electromagnetic theory, one obtained an incorrect radiation law. Once again physicists had come across a case in which the laws of physics were violated drastically.

Planck does not seem to have fully grasped the significance of this postulate. For it implied no less than that radiation was emitted and absorbed in the form of "quanta" hf. Einstein was

---

*These were usually thought of as electrons bound to equilibrium positions.

the first who understood, and he used it in 1905 to explain the photoelectric effect. Photoelectric effect is the emission of electrons from suitably chosen surfaces under the influence of light.* According to electromagnetic theory, one would expect the energy of the emitted electrons to depend upon the light *intensity*. The experiments did not verify this expectation, but they showed instead that no electrons were emitted unless the frequency f of the incident radiation exceeded a critical frequency f_0, which depended upon the emitting surface under study. At higher frequencies f the energy of the emitted electrons was found not to exceed a maximum value E_{MAX}. The value of E_{MAX} was found to be proportional to the frequency f, and the proportionality factor was found to be independent of the surface under study. Einstein expressed these results by the equation:

$$E_{MAX} = hf - hf_0 \text{ ; or } hf = E_{MAX} + hf_0 \quad (1)$$

and interpreted hf_0 as the minimum amount of energy needed to liberate an electron from the surface and hf as the energy supplied by the radiation. Careful measurements showed that the value of h obtained from this effect agreed with the value obtained from black body radiation data. One was thus forced to a dual concept of light: Some experiments led to the conclusion that light was a wave phenomenon, others that it should be considered as a stream of particles.

2. Understanding atomic spectra and atomic structure[1-2].

Bohr showed in 1913 how these ideas could be made fruitful in the interpretation of the characteristic spectra emitted by the atoms of the various elements. It was known since 1882

---

*This effect has found important practical applications in light-sensitive devices such as photoelectric cells, pick-up tubes for television cameras, etc.

that the wavelengths λ of the emitted radiation of hydrogen atoms could be represented as:

$$1/\lambda = R(1/m^2 - 1/n^2) \qquad (2)$$

with $m = 1, 2, \ldots$ and $n = m + 1, m + 2, \ldots$, where R is a constant. Bohr showed that this formula could be derived from the following postulates:

1. There are stable circular orbits in which the electron does not radiate (to account for the stability of the atoms).

2. In those stable orbits the angular momentum P is an integral number times $h/2\pi$ (quantization):

$$P = n(h/2\pi) \, (n = 1, 2, \ldots) \qquad (3)$$

It may be shown that these values of P correspond to energies:

$$E_n = -Rhc/n^2 \, (n = 1, 2, \ldots) \qquad (4)$$

where R can be expressed in terms of atomic constants and c is the velocity of light. The energy E_n is negative, since the electron is *bound* to the atom.

3. When a transition takes place between stable orbits (quantum jump), radiation is emitted or absorbed in the form of a quantum hf. The quantum emitted equals the difference in energy:

$$hf = E_n - E_m \qquad (5)$$

Substituting (4) into (5) and bearing in mind that $f = c/\lambda$ yields (2). Balmer's formula (2), that had baffled physicists for more than 30 years, had been explained.

This theory was easily applied to more complex atoms. Postulate 3 applied immediately. Instead of postulate 1 one had to assume more general (elliptic) orbits. To find the correct extension of postulate 2 one had to generalize the method of quantization such that the quantization of the hydrogen atom and of the harmonic oscillator ($E_n = nhf$, $n = 0, 1, 2,$

. . . .) followed from it as special cases. After this was done, it was found that the orbits should be measured by two "quantum numbers" n and l ($n = 1, 2, \ldots$; $l = 0, 1, 2, \ldots$, $n - 1$) where n measured the average distance to the nucleus and l the ellipticity of the orbit and the angular momentum.

This knowledge allowed to interpret many of the features of spectra in the visible and in the X-ray region. Spectra in the visible or the near-visible region are caused by transitions of outer electrons between outlying orbits. Little energy is needed to excite these spectra; the heat of hot flames or the energy of relatively slow electrons is sufficient. The study of these spectra allowed thus to probe the outer layers of the atom. To probe the deeper layers of the atom, where the more firmly bound electrons are located, one has to use more energy. The necessary information is contained in the characteristic X-rays emitted by the atoms. These X-rays are emitted if a more firmly bound electron is kicked out of the atom by a fast electron colliding with it. Electrons from outer orbits then make a transition to the inner empty orbit under emission of an X-ray quantum.

These studies gave a fairly good understanding of the structure of the atom. But some details of the observations could not be interpreted by the two quantum numbers n and l. It turned out that the missing clues could be obtained from the influence of a magnetic field upon the emitted light. That such an effect existed was not so surprising, for an electron moving in an orbit is equivalent to a current flowing in a closed loop. It should thus behave as a tiny magnet that should be influenced by a magnetic field. The experiments showed that the orbit of an electron characterized by the number l could have ($2l + 1$) possible orientations in a magnetic field, all with slightly different energies. A new quantum number m_l ($m_l = -l, -l + 1 ; \ldots \ldots , l - 1, l$) was thus introduced to describe these orientations. It also turned out that the electron itself was spinning around its axis and behaved as a tiny magnet that was found to have two possible orientations in a magnetic field. Hence a quantum number m_s ($m_s = -\frac{1}{2}, +\frac{1}{2}$) was introduced to describe these orientations. The individual "orbits" of the electrons and their relative orientation were now characterized by the four quantum numbers n, l, m_l, m_s.

This theory gave many more orbit combinations with different energies than were actually observed. There was apparently some principle that restricted them. Pauli formulated this restriction as: "No two electrons in an atom can have the same set of quantum numbers" (Pauli's exclusion principle). This turned out to give the correct number of electron orbits. It also provided the key to the understanding of the periodic system of elements.

In addition there were apparently restrictions in the transitions between orbits, since not all possible transitions were actually detected by their light emission. Soon one learned to read these "selection rules" from the spectra and by intelligent guessing succeeded in fully unraveling the structure of the atom. The whole development was practically completed in 1925.

3. Conclusions.

When one looks at these developments, it is difficult to suppress admiration for the skill with which the physicists of those days carried out their task. True enough, many questions remained unanswered. They did not know why there were stable orbits, why the selection rules held and why Pauli's exclusion principle was valid. Nevertheless, they found practically all the keys to the structure of the atom.

At the same time their method of approach began to change. The approach to physics became more phenomenological and it became better understood that the information was all there, provided that one learned to ask the right questions. There was less dogmatism in physics and a greater willingness to exchange old ideas for new ones. One did no longer hesitate to use seemingly contradictory approaches to problems. The dual character of light, in which both corpuscular and wave descriptions were used freely (see next chapter), was the first case in physics where such an approach was necessary.

Physics is not a discipline that is developed in a straightforward manner without a flaw, as one might sometimes think when reading popular biographies of famous scientists. Progress can be painfully slow and the method of attacking the unknown is often better described as "feeling one's way ahead" than as a glorious march to victory. Such an approach is not uncommon in theology. The German theologian Hans Asmussen has described that situation by the same expression "Vorantasten." This is, of course, only an analogy in the method of approach used in the two fields.

The physicists of the early 20th century did not believe that their difficulties would be removed overnight, but they were confident that ultimately the pieces of the puzzle would be put together. In 1925 Max Born published a book entitled: "Vorlesungen uber Atommechanik," Vol. I. In the preface he expressed the hope that some day he would be able to write volume II in which the things that could not yet be explained would find their proper explanation. In his opinion such a development might be many years away. Actually most problems were solved the following year with the advent of wave mechanics.

REFERENCES:

[1]S. Glasstone, *Sourcebook On Atomic Energy*, Van Nostrand, 1958. (Contains also a relatively simple account of the beginnings of the theory of quanta and of the structure of the atom.)

[2]A. d'Arbro, *The Rise of the New Physics*, Vol. II, Dover Publications, New York, 1951. (Discusses relativity and the quantum theory.)

CHAPTER NINE

Waves and Particles
Wave Mechanics

Since one can visualize water waves, the "wave" concept is not a difficult one. When it is said, however, that light or material particles sometimes show wave character, this is not so easily visualized. The analogy with water waves is only in the mathematical description.

Neither is the "particle" concept a difficult one. When it is said, however, that light must be considered as a stream of "light particles" or quanta, this is not so easily visualized. The analogy is here in the fact that the quanta are more or less localized bits of energy, such in contrast with uninterrupted waves, in which the energy is distributed over space. When one goes to the realm of the almost infinitely small and states that electrons are "particles," this is not so easily visualized either. What is meant is, that the electron is a more or less localized bit of mass.

Experiments indicate the dual character of light and matter. Some experiments must be interpreted by means of wave concepts and others by particle concepts. The two concepts can be unified mathematically by means of the concept of the "wave pulse," that is, an interrupted wave. A very short "wave pulse" has in common with a "particle" that its position and its energy are more or less localized. It is wrong to say that a more or less localized quantum or electron *is* a wave pulse. All one can say is, that it is *represented* by a wave pulse. It turns out that a consistent mathematical theory, known as "wave mechanics," can be built with the help of this representation.

Representation of particles by wave pulses implies a mathematical relationship known as Heisenberg's uncertainty principle. Since exaggerated claims are made about this principle, the chapter starts with a short and somewhat mathematical discussion about what the "wave pulse" approach implies.

1. Waves and particles. Heisenberg's uncertainty principle[1-7].

In classical physics light had been considered as a wave phenomenon to be described by the frequency f and (or) the *wavelength* λ. This had been backed up by interference experiments which indicated that light plus light can give darkness. The new developments in atomic physics showed, however, that light was emitted and absorbed in the form of quanta of energy $E = hf$. Later it was discovered that emission, absorption and scattering of light could be described as a collision process in which the quantum carried a momentum $p = hf/c$, where $c = f\lambda$ is the velocity of light. From these results, or from earlier relativity theory, it could be deduced that a quantum had a mass $m = hf/c^2 = E/c^2$. The "particle" attributes of the quantum were thus complete.

There was thus a duality in physics; light had both wave and particle character. Some experiments could best be described by a "particle" approach (emission, absorption and scattering of light), other experiments were best described by a "wave" approach (interference and polarization experiments), whereas a third group of experiments could be described either way (light pressure, Doppler effect). Just as the "particle character" of the light is characterized by the energy E and the momentum p of the quantum, so the "wave character" of the light can be characterized by the frequency f and the wavelength $\lambda = c/f$ of the waves. This duality can be expressed by the equations:

$$E = mc^2 = hf \text{, or: } f = E/h$$
$$p = hf/c = h/\lambda \text{, or: } \lambda = h/p \qquad (1)$$

To state that the two points of view *contradict* each other is too strong. It is better to say that they *complement* each other. However, it must be admitted that it is not so easy to visualize something that can exhibit both particle and wave character.

Was there also a similar duality for material particles? If so, then one would expect the relations between the energy E and the frequency f and between the momentum p and the wavelength λ to be identical with the relations holding for quanta:

$$f = E/h \; ; \lambda = h/p \qquad (1a)$$

De Broglie made this suggestion in 1924 and was able to show how this led to Bohr's second postulate. Quantization thus appeared to be a direct consequence of the wave character of the particle. Later the wave character of material particles was demonstrated experimentally by interference experiments and the equation for λ was verified. This indicated the corresponding dual character of material particles.

How can this dual character of waves and particles be incorporated into a mathematical theory? It is easily seen that a *wave pulse* might accomplish this. It retains the wave character of the phenomenon and at the same time localizes it more or less. This turns out to be the approach that gives correct results. The theory that develops and applies this idea is known as *wave mechanics.*

The mathematical representation of a particle by a wave pulse has mathematical implications, as will now be demonstrated. First consider the wave pulse at a certain position in space as a function of *time.* It may be shown mathematically that such a wave pulse can be represented as a superposition of continuous waves of different *frequency* (Fourier's theorem). For a wave pulse of duration Δt most of these continuous waves have frequencies lying with a range Δf around a center frequency f_0, such that:

$$\Delta f \cdot \Delta t \geqq 1/2\pi \qquad (2)$$

($\geqq$ means larger than or equal to). The shorter the duration of the pulse the less accurate the frequency of the wave can be known.

Next consider the wave pulse at a given time as a function of *position.* According to Fourier's theorem such a wave pulse can be represented as a superposition of continuous waves of different *wavelength.* For a wave pulse of length Δx most of these continuous waves have wave numbers $1/\lambda$ ($=$ number of waves per unit length) lying within the range $\Delta(1/\lambda)$ around the center wave number $1/\lambda_0$, such that:

$$\Delta(1/\lambda) \cdot \Delta x \geqq 1/2\pi \qquad (2a)$$

The shorter the wave pulse, the less accurate its wave number can be known.

There is nothing mysterious about these relations; they are mathematical inequalities holding for any arbitrary phenomenon that can be described by a wave pulse. They form the basis of television and radar, and nobody attaches any deep philosophical or theological implications to them.

Things are claimed to become quite different, however, if both sides of these equations are multiplied by Planck's constant h. Observing that $\Delta E = h\Delta f$ is the inaccuracy in energy E associated with the inaccuracy Δf in frequency and that $\Delta p = h\Delta(1/\lambda)$ is the inaccuracy in momentum p associated with the inaccuracy $\Delta(1/\lambda)$ in wave number then yields:

$$\Delta E \cdot \Delta t \geqq h/2\pi; \quad \Delta p \cdot \Delta x \geqq h/2\pi \qquad (3)$$

These inequalities are known as *Heisenberg's uncertainty relations*. It has been claimed that they have important philosophical and theological implications. Such a claim seems odd, since equations (3) are a consequence of two mathematical inequalities that have no such implications. It has also been claimed that equations (3) emphasize once again the fundamental nature of Planck's constant h. This is not fully correct, for Planck's constant enters in more or less accidentally. Mathematically speaking, the fundamental inequalities are (2) and (2a), which have nothing to do with Planck's constant. The latter is only introduced in order to rewrite the inequalities in terms of the more accessible physical quantities: energy and time and momentum and position.

It is understandable that the enunciation of the inequalities (3) caused considerable criticism. Various paper experiments* were proposed that were supposed to show how Heisenberg's uncertainty principle could be violated. A careful analysis of such proposals always indicated that the uncertainty principle was valid.

Similar paper experiments aim at defining theoretical state-

---

*I have called these experiments "paper" experiments, since nobody had any intention of carrying them out. They are just used as illustrations in the discussion of the validity or invalidity of Heisenberg's uncertainty principle.

ments operationally. For example, in a theoretical analysis one often states: "Let an electron be located in the point (x, y, z)." The paper experiment then demonstrates how to locate a particle accurately. Or it is stated: "Let an electron have the speed v." The paper experiment then demonstrates how to measure velocity accurately. Again a careful analysis shows that Heisenberg's uncertainty principle is valid.

Actually the outcome of such discussions is not at all surprising, since the inequalities (3) are the consequences of the mathematical relationships (2) and (2a). They hold as soon as one has learned about the dual character of waves and particles. It is even immaterial whether or not the wave pulse presentation of the particle is the *only* presentation available. All that is needed is that it is a *permissible* presentation, for in that case all other presentations must give the same result.

2.   Wave mechanics[1-7].

It was now clear that the motion of a particle had to be described as a wave motion. Wave motion is generally described by a differential equation known as the *wave* equation. Because of differences between "light waves" and "matter waves," the equations for the two should be similar but not necessarily fully identical. Schrödinger found the proper wave equation in 1926 and applied it to atomic problems. Soon a number of successes had been obtained. For example the theory showed that there are stable "energy states" or "energy levels," in which the atoms do not radiate, it verified the rules of quantization and the selection rules, allowed to understand Pauli's exclusion principle and gave a host of other interesting results.

That discrete energy levels exist for an electron in an atom can be made plausible with the help of a wave picture.

Besides free running waves and wave pulses one can also have *standing* waves. Such waves underlie the operation of musical instruments such as organs, violins, etc. An organ pipe of a given size gives a well-defined tone determined by its standing-wave pattern. In the same manner the discrete energies of an electron in an atom are a consequence of different "standing wave patterns" in the atom.

One of the consequences of the uncertainty principle is that one can no longer speak of "electron orbits" in an atom. The electron is more or less "smeared out" over space. The theory only gives the probability of finding the electron in a given volume element close to the nucleus. A localized charge moving around the nucleus radiates energy according to classical theory, but a smeared-out charge does not. The "smeared-out" condition of the electron thus makes plausible why the electron does not radiate if it is in a stable energy state.

The uncertainty principle also illustrates why many predictions of wave mechanics are of a statistical nature. Classically, one can predict the future as soon as the laws and the initial conditions are known. Wave mechanically speaking, however, one knows the laws but cannot know the initial position and velocity of an electron with absolute accuracy. Consequently, one cannot predict exactly where an electron will be at a later instant. One can only give the probability of finding it in any particular place.

This should not cause any alarm, however. Planck's constant is small and as a consequence the uncertainty principle makes itself felt only at the atomic or near-atomic level. At the macroscopic level the laws of classical mechanics are valid. Those who go deer hunting and miss their deer should not blame

Heisenberg's uncertainty principle but should attribute their bad luck to bad shooting.

Wave mechanics gave a physical basis for one of the commonest forces that hold a molecule together, the so-called *homopolar bond.* In contrast with it, the theory of the *ionic* bond can be given on a classical basis.

In a simple ionic compound XY the atom Y has lost one electron to the X-atom so that the compound can be written as X^-Y^+. At large distances between the ions the only force is thus the electrostatic attraction. When the "electron clouds" surrounding the two ions start to penetrate each other, repulsion predominates. An equilibrium distance will thus be attained so that the two opposing forces balance.

Most molecules are not held together by an ionic type of bond but by a homopolar bond. To explain this type of bond, one considers in the simplest case each atom as consisting of a positive ion and an electron. At large distances each electron belongs to the proper ion, but at shorter distances the two ions more or less share the two electrons by mutually exchanging them. As a consequence of the wave character of the particles, this exchange can occur in two ways:

a) So that the net electron charge density between the two positive ions is relatively small. In that case ion repulsion predominates.

b) So that the net electron charge density between the two ions is relatively large. In this case the attractive forces predominate.

The latter is the cause of the homopolar bond. The interaction is purely electrostatic in character but to evaluate it one has to apply wave mechanics. Because of the exchange of electrons involved in the interaction it is known as *exchange* interaction.

Wave mechanics could also give a successful theory of radioactive decay. As an example, consider a radioactive element that spontaneously emits doubly charged helium ions (α-particles). Experimentally it is found that the nuclei decay at a rate that is characteristic for the nuclear species under study. Such a phenomenon cannot be understood on a classical basis.

The process can be illustrated by the following analogy. The α-particle moving inside the nucleus and bound to the nucleus can be compared with a marble oscillating in a bowl with so little energy that it cannot reach the rim of the bowl and escape. According to the laws of classical physics the marble should thus stay inside the bowl forever. But if the motion of the marble must be considered as a wave motion, the marble can indeed escape, since the wave does not have to pass *over the rim* of the bowl, but can escape by passing *through the wall* of the bowl. In that case one cannot predict theoretically *when* the marble will escape, but one can calculate the *probability* that it escapes.

The wave-mechanical theory of radioactive decay can predict the probability that decay occurs. The predicted rates of decay agree quite well with experiment, so that it is fair to conclude that wave mechanics can give a quantitative theory of the decay. The theory also illustrates the statistical character of the predictions made by wave mechanics.

3. Conclusions drawn from the uncertainty principles[1-3-7].

It is understandable that the drastic changes in the physical sciences at the atomic level, brought about by the advent of wave mechanics, gave rise to a considerable discussion about the philosophical and theological implications involved.

For example, it has been said that wave mechanics violates the principle of causality and leads to a non-causal description of nature. Actually this is not true. Causality allows to predict future behavior of a system if the laws and the initial conditions of the system are known and to attribute future behavior to the laws and the initial conditions. According to wave mechanics, however, we cannot know *all* the initial conditions with unlimited exactness because of Heisenberg's uncertainty principle. As a consequence not all aspects of future behavior can be predicted with unlimited accuracy either. The limited accuracy is a consequence of our lack of full knowledge of the initial conditions. This is as causal a description as can be given under the existing circumstances.

A particular important case is that of an "elementary event," such as a collision between an electron and a particle, the radioactive decay of a nucleus or the transition of an atom from a higher energy state to a lower energy state. The theory does not predict when a particular elementary event takes place. It only predicts its probability. To call it "events without a cause," as is sometimes done, is misleading. All that can be said is that the theory cannot make any further predictions than are given by the calculated probabilities.

David Bohm[7] has suggested that a strictly causal description of atomic phenomena can be given if "hidden variables" are introduced. This would mean then that in atomic experiments one does not control all the factors contributing to its outcome, so that the final result of the measurements shows random fluctuations. Nobody would conclude from it that the principle of causality is violated here. Whether or not Bohm's suggestions are correct depends on how these hidden variables are introduced. If they are introduced in such a manner that

Heisenberg's uncertainty principle and the wave equation are upheld, it just means a change in "windowdressing" that does not alter the content of the theory.

It has been said that Heisenberg's principle allows the human will to be *free*. That is a questionable statement, the result of a long extrapolation. In the first place, it is uncertain that the concepts taken from physics are suitable for this problem, for the physicist enters a realm completely different from his own when discussing the problem of free will. In the second place, though it is undoubtedly true that making decisions involves physical processes both in the thinking and the deciding, it is not certain that these processes *determine* our decisions, since they may only accompany them.* But even if physical processes determined our decisions, then the uncertainty in our *description* of physical processes does not necessarily mean that there is an uncertainty in nature itself (see Bohm). Finally, though we shall see that quantum phenomena can make themselves felt at a macroscopic level in some biological processes, that does not guarantee sufficient freedom for the human will. A physicist thinking about human free will has to learn new ideas and new modes of thinking if he wants to contribute to the problem.

It has also been claimed that the observer interacts with the object and determines its response. This is an inaccurate statement. What is really meant is an application to the atomic domain of the obvious fact that the experimental arrangement determines the outcome of the experiment. It is merely another illustration of the dual character of light and of material particles.

---

*For example, if I want to hit somebody with my hand, then the motion of my hand does not *determine* my decision but executes it. The only thing that the motion of my hand *does* determine, is whether or not I will be successful.

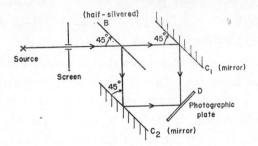

This problem will be discussed for the experimental set-up shown in the figure. It consists of a light source, a slit S, a half-silvered mirror* B, two mirrors C_1 and C_2 and a photographic plate D. If the light along the path BC_1 or along the path BC_2 is intercepted, one observes a certain blackening pattern on the photographic plate, which can be described on a quantum basis.** For if the beam BC_2 is intercepted, one may say: "The quantum causing the blackening of the silver halide grain of the plate D traveled along the path SBC_1D." But if the light is not intercepted in either path, the blackening on the plate D shows an interference pattern in which regions of minimum blackening alternate with regions of maximum blackening. This cannot be described by the quantum concept alone. For one cannot understand how a *particle* can travel along two different paths simultaneously and how light plus light can give darkness on a quantum basis. The interference pattern must be described by the wave theory. But this theory, in turn, cannot give a full description of the phenomena either, since the blackening of the plate is a quantum effect. *Both* the wave and the quantum approach are needed for a full description of the observed phenomena.

*This is a mirror that passes half the light and reflects the other half.

**This is not a *full* quantum description, however, since the light beam passing through each slit is broadened by diffraction effects.

Now let the exposure time be made so short that only *one* quantum arrives at the plate during that time. In that case the quantum will not give an interference pattern on the plate, but it will give a blackening at some spot on the plate. A following quantum may give a blackening at another spot on the plate. Only if a large number of quanta is used, does one obtain a full interference pattern. The wave theory thus predicts with what *probability* a certain spot on the plate is hit by a particle, but it does not determine the "actual path taken" by the particle. The latter is an inadmissible concept that has no place in our description.

The experimental arrangement just shown does not determine what is going to *happen* at B. It only allows us to *predict* what will be observed at D if a sufficiently large number of quanta is involved. The outcome of an experiment with a *single* quantum, a so-called elementary event, cannot be predicted. The theoretically predicted probability distribution of the quanta arriving at D can be verified experimentally by repeating the event many times.

It would be wrong to conclude from experiments like the one just mentioned that the observer *interferes* with the object. It only demonstrates how the final outcome of the experiment depends upon the experimental arrangement and illustrates the dual character of our description of waves and particles. This does not deny that the experimental set-up may interfere with the object. As a matter of fact, this is often the sole reason for doing the experiment.

4. Quantum effects in biology[2].

Pascual Jordan has pointed out how quantum effects can make themselves felt at a macroscopic level in many biological phenomena. He has called this the "amplifier theory" of quantum effects.

As a first example, consider the killing of living cells by high-energy radiation, either consisting of particles or quanta. The killing occurs because the incoming radiation produces ion pairs in the irradiated material. It has been found that the production of a single ion pair in a well-defined area of the cell is sufficient to kill the cell. Since the production of an ion pair by the incoming radiation is a quantum effect, we see that a single elementary event occurring at the atomic level produces a macroscopic effect: the death of the cell.

Still more drastic is the effect in the case of radiation-induced mutations. The hereditary character of plants and animals is determined by the chromosomes of the cells that take part in the reproduction and is located in tiny parts of the chromosomes, the so-called *genes*. One single elementary event, the production of an ion pair or the absorption of a small amount of some form of energy, is sufficient to relocate an atom or atom group in a gene. The resulting change in the hereditary characteristics of the specimen involved is known as a *mutation*. Some of these mutations are lethal, the fertilized ovum dies, similar to what was found in the previous case. In many other instances, however, the offspring lives. A single quantum effect has then produced a whole new variety of animals or plants.

A still larger effect involves all living material on earth. One of the chief characteristics of living material is its ability to reproduce its basic building blocks: the protein molecules. If a chemist makes organic molecules such as proteins, they can occur in two forms that are each other's mirror image. Since there is no preference for the one form or the other, both types of molecules are made roughly in equal numbers. But in living tissue one finds, surprising enough, only one of the two mirror-image forms. Jordan thus draws the conclusion that the occurrence of life must have been a unique event involving *one single* first molecule that obtained the property of reproducing itself. Since it occurred in *one* of the two forms, all the offspring was necessarily of that form. If life had started at many places on earth simultaneously, this would not have been the case. Jordan thus concludes: " . . . . , so kann man die historische Wurzel der tatsächlich eingetretenen Bevorzügung nur in einem Vorgang *ohne Uhrsache suchen*—dass heisst in einem mikrophysikalischen Einzelerreignis.*"

5. Complementarity in physics and in theology.

The wave-mechanical description of atomic particles presented the first case in physics where two seemingly contradictory points of view were united into a single theory and thus complemented each other. In theology this is not uncommon. Theologians have long been accustomed to work with seemingly contradictory concepts (the Trinity, the two natures of Christ, God's love and God's justice, . . . etc.) People that are accustomed to contradiction-free systems of thinking often have considerable difficulty in grasping the necessity of such an approach. Let us illustrate this approach with two examples: the trinitarian doctrine established by the councils meetings in Nicaea (325), Alexandria (362) and Constantinople (381) and the doctrine of the two natures of Christ established by the council meeting in Chalcedon (451).

---

*". . . hence, one can only find the historical reason for the preference that actually occurred in an event without cause—that is, in a microphysical elementary event." For the term "without cause" see section 9.3. The present state of our knowledge does not allow to give any further specification of this "event."

Before we do so, however, a word of caution is in order. The analogy between physics and theology at this point is only one in *method* of approach. Also, the analogy is not a complete one, for in physics one can always hope (as some do) that sooner or later the duality will be removed when new data are obtained or new points of view arise. In theology that would be extremely unlikely. Finally, the discussion is not given for the unnecessary apologetical purpose of making the two doctrines more plausible or more palatable. As long as these restrictions are born in mind, however, it may be worth while to make the comparison.

The first dealt with the relation between God the Father, Jesus Christ the Son, and the Holy Spirit. It cannot be denied that the Bible speaks of all three. It was not clear in the early Church, however, how the relation between the three should be confessed. Was there only one God and were the Son and the Holy Spirit not divine, or were there three Gods? The councils decided that the *one* God has revealed Himself as the Father, the Son and the Holy Spirit and that the Father, the Son and the Holy Spirit *together* are one God. They established the short formula: "One God, three Persons, Unity in substance." According to the Athanasian creed: "We honor the one God in the Trinity and the Trinity in the Unity, without mixing the persons or dividing the substance."*

Seemingly contradictory concepts are here used together and these seeming contradictions have caused considerable misunderstanding. Any attempt to remove these "contradictions," however, would either lead to confessing the Unity and denying the Trinity or to denying the Unity and confessing the

---

*The word "person" is here used in a sense that is somewhat different from common-day usage. This sometimes causes misunderstandings that cannot be dealt with here.

Trinity. Facing this dilemma the Christian Church had no other choice but protecting both and that is what the short formula tries to do. It is thus not an attempt to "explain" the mystery surrounding God. On the contrary, it refrains from any "explanation" and thereby protects the mystery. This is an example of complementary thinking.

The second doctrine dealt with the relationship between the divine and the human nature of Christ. The earlier councils had confessed that Jesus Christ was true God. But the Church also confessed that Christ was true man (Incarnation!). The question was how the two were related. Were there two natures of Christ or were there two persons (the concept "person" being used in the same sense as in the discussion of the Trinity)? Were the two natures of Christ of equal rank or was the one subordinated over the other? The difficulty was again to confess in such a manner that all the aspects of the Biblical teaching were maintained. This was impossible in an "either-or" statement; an "and-and" statement was needed here. The council of Chalcedon therefore established that in Christ there were "two natures in one person, unmixed and unchanged, undivided and unseparated." One should note once more that this is not an attempt to "explain" Christ, but much more a decision *not* to explain in order to safeguard the truth.

Again, seemingly contradictory concepts are used together to guard the truth, to confess the unity of Christ and to acknowledge the divine and the human nature of Christ equally. As Schrey[8] puts it: "Die wahre Gottheit und die wahre Menschheit können nur dann zusammen ausgesagt werden wenn keiner von beiden etwas abgebrochen wird."* This is complementary thinking. Schrey expresses this nicely as follows: "Zur wesen

---

*The true deity and the true humanity can only then be expressed simultaneously when nothing is subtracted from either one.

der Komplementarität gehört dass erst das Zusammen von zwei angeblich und scheinbar sich widersprechenden Grössen das wahre Bild der Wirklichkeit gibt."*

More examples could be given. As a matter of fact, most Biblical exegesis that is true to its source uses a complementary form of approach. Bonhoeffer's little book "Versuchung" is an excellent example of it.**

One should be careful, however, not to apply this concept indiscriminately. It must be investigated first whether the concept really applies and whether the two points of view that are united are really seemingly contradictory. Two points of view that are only remotely connected and not contradictory should not be cited as an example of complementarity, even though they "complement" each other in the normal sense of the word. It is then better to say that the new point of view adds another "dimension" to our thinking.*** A physicist studying literature, history, or theology, for example, enters into a world quite different from the one in which he is doing this daily task. Other dimensions open up to him when he does so.

---

*It belongs to the essence of complementarity that only two supposedly and seemingly contradictory quantities together give the true picture of reality.

**D. Bonhoeffer, Versuchung, Kaiser Verlag, München, 1953.

***Viewed from this angle, all monistic systems suffer from the fact that they are "one-dimensional."

REFERENCES:
[1] W. Heisenberg, Das Naturbild der heutigen Physik, Rowohlt, Hamburg, 1955.
[2] P. Jordan, Das Bild der modernen Physik, Ullstein, Frankfurt, 1957.
[3] A. March, Die physikalische Erkenntnis und ihre Grenzen, Vieweg & Sohn, Braunschweig, 1955.
[4] W. Heisenberg, Physics and Philosophy, Harper and Brothers, New York, 1958.
[5] N. Bohr, Atomic Physics and Human Knowledge, John Wiley & Sons, 1958.
[6] A. Einstein and L. Infeld, The Evolution of Physics, Simon and Schuster, 1942.
[7] D. Bohm, Causality and Chance in Modern Physics, l.c.
[8] H. H. Schrey, Weltbild und Glaube im 20 Jahrhundert, Göttingen, 1955.

CHAPTER TEN

Nuclear Physics

In order to understand the peaceful and military uses of atomic energy it is necessary to give a somewhat detailed technical discussion of nuclear physics. The applications of atomic energy and its moral and religious implications are discussed in the next few chapters.

1. Historical development[1].

After having deciphered the structure of the atoms, it became evident that most of the mass of the atoms was contained in its nucleus. As a matter of fact, the electrons moving around it contribute less than 0.1% to the total mass. The chemical behavior of the atom is determined by the number Z of electrons moving around the nucleus or, what amounts to the same thing, by the electric charge $+ Ze$ of the nucleus, where $- e$ is the electric charge of an electron. The integral number Z is known as the *atomic number*. It was further discovered that not all nuclei of a given chemical element, characterized by Z, had the same mass.

After sensitive methods for comparing atomic masses had

been developed, it became known that all atoms had masses that were approximately an integral number times the mass of a hydrogen ion, also known by the name "proton." To characterize the mass of an atom, one thus introduced a second integral number: the *mass number A*. Atomic nuclei with the same value of Z but different values of A, the so-called *isotopes*, have the same chemical properties but different weight. Atomic nuclei with different values of Z but the same A, the so-called *isobars*, have different chemical properties but the same weight. A nucleus is thus fully identified by the two numbers Z and A. The fact that the masses of all nuclei were integral numbers times the mass of the proton, indicated that protons might be an important constituent of atomic nuclei.

A nucleus of the chemical element X is represented by the symbol $_ZX^A$. The proton is represented by the symbols $_1H^1$ and $_1p^1$. In this notation an electron is written as $_{-1}e^0$ and a positive electron as $_1e^0$. The latter particle occurs in some nuclear reactions.

It had also been found that most of the nuclei of isotopes of the elements with Z larger than 82 ($Z = 82$ is lead) were unstable and emitted radiation, first distinguished as α-, β-, and γ-radiation (natural radioactivity). The α-radiation was found to consist of high speed helium nuclei ($_2He^4$). The β-radiation consisted of high speed electrons ($_{-1}e^0$). The γ-radiation was found to consist of high energy quanta of well-defined energies characteristic for the nuclei under study. It thus seemed that both helium nuclei and electrons were present inside the nuclei and that the nucleus could assume discrete energies (energy levels) with energy differences much larger than those between the energy levels of the atoms.

Another important step in the understanding of the structure of atomic nuclei came from the discovery of the transmutation of the nuclei by the bombardment of fast particles, putting into effect the dream of the old alchemists. First helium nuclei from naturally radioactive samples were used. The first reaction studied was the transmutation of nitrogen ($_7N^{14}$) into oxygen ($_8O^{17}$) that can be represented as*:

$$_7N^{14} + _2He^4 \rightarrow _8O^{17} + _1H^1$$

Soon many more examples were found.

Later physicists learned to accelerate charged particles to higher and higher energies. This made it possible to use other atomic projectiles such as *protons* ($_1H^1$), as well as helium nuclei ($_2He^4$) and electrons ($_{-1}e^0$). The first reaction studied was the disintegration of the lithium nucleus $_3Li^7$, represented by the reaction equation:

$$_3Li^7 + _1H^1 \rightarrow _2He^4 + _2He^4$$

The study of nuclear reactions was helped considerably by the development of the *Wilson cloud chamber*. This research tool made the tracks of the fast particles used in nuclear reactions, or emerging from nuclear reactions, visible. It is possible to identify the various particles (protons, electrons, etc.) from the observed tracks.

In 1932 a new particle, the neutron, was discovered in a nuclear reaction between helium nuclei ($_2He^4$) and beryllium nuclei ($_4Be^9$). The two nuclei combined to form a stable carbon nucleus ($_6C^{12}$) under emission of a neutron. The neutron has a mass approximately equal to the mass of a hydrogen nucleus. It has zero charge and is therefore represented by the symbol $_0n^1$. The reaction involved can be written as:

$$_4Be^9 + _2He^4 \rightarrow _6C^{12} + _0n^1$$

---

*In such a reaction equation the sum of the atomic numbers on each side must be equal (law of conservation of charge) and the same must be true for the sum of the mass numbers (law of conservation of mass).

The neutron is an unstable particle. Left free, it decays into a proton and an electron according to the process:

$$_0n^1 \rightarrow {}_1H^1 + {}_{-1}e^0$$

The half life of a free neutron is about 13 minutes, that is, after about 13 minutes half of the free neutrons have decayed. Most neutrons disappear, however, by being captured by other nuclei. For slow neutrons this capture process can be represented as:

$$_ZX^A + {}_0n^1 \rightarrow {}_ZX^{A+1} + \gamma\text{-radiation}$$

It thus transforms a nucleus into its next heavier isotope.

Neutrons have become very important projectiles for effecting nuclear transmutations. The reason why they are more effective than charged particles is that the latter are repelled by the positively charged nucleus, whereas this repulsive force does not exist for neutrons. The role played by neutrons in nuclear reactions indicated that they might be an important constituent of the nuclei.

2. Nuclear theory[1].

Before the discovery of the neutron it was thought that the nucleus $_ZX^A$ consisted of A protons and $(A - Z)$ electrons, in total thus $(2A - Z)$ particles. The proved existence of the neutron also allowed the possibility that the nucleus consisted of Z protons and $(A - Z)$ neutrons, or in total A particles. The two alternatives should give different values for the angular momentum of some nuclei and this gave a possibility to discriminate between the two.

It was known from spectroscopical data that the proton was spinning around its axis with an angular momentum equal to that of an electron. If the proton-electron model of the nucleus were true, the possible values of the angular momentum of any nucleus could be predicted from those of its constituents. The observed angular momenta of the nuclei $_1H^2$ (deuteron), $_3Li^6$ (lithium), $_5B^{10}$ (boron) and $_7N^{14}$ (nitrogen) were found to be absolutely incompatible with the proton-electron model. The observed angular momenta could be readily explained with the help of the proton-neutron model of the nucleus, if it were assumed that the neutron had the same angular momentum as the proton. The nuclei thus consist of protons and neutrons. For example, the deuteron ($_1H^2$) consists of one proton and one neutron bound together.

Why can a neutron be stable *inside* the nucleus? For the simple reason that it is *not* free. Some nuclei formed under bombardment by fast particles are unstable and decay under emission of positive and negative electrons (artificial radioactivity). Some naturally radioactive elements decay under emission of a negative electron, whereas still other nuclei can capture one of the outer electrons (orbital electron capture). If none of these three processes is energetically possible, the nucleus is stable.

Emission of a negative electron means that the nucleus $_zX^A$ changes into the next higher isobar $_{z+1}W^A$. Emission of a positive electron means that the nucleus $_zX^A$ changes into the next lower isobar $_{z-1}W^A$ and orbital electron capture gives rise to the same change. These changes can be represented by the following reactions inside the nucleus, respectively:

$$_0n^1 \rightarrow {}_1p^1 + {}_{-1}e^0$$
$$_1p^1 \rightarrow {}_0n^1 + {}_1e^0$$
$$_1p^1 + {}_{-1}e^0 \rightarrow {}_0n^1$$

The mass of a nucleus is smaller than the sum of the masses of its constituents, as a consequence of Einstein's mass-energy relation. For the nucleus is held together by strong forces. An amount of work ΔE has to be done to separate the nucleus into its constituents, and as a consequence an energy ΔE is set free if the protons and the neutrons are brought together to form the nucleus. But this means that the mass of the nucleus is smaller by an amount $\Delta M = \Delta E / c^2$ than the sum of the masses of its constituents.

The energy law and the momentum law are accurately satisfied in the following nuclear reactions:

a) Reactions involving heavy particles (protons, neutrons, helium ions). Here Einstein's relation between mass and energy has to be taken into account in the energy balance.

b) Nuclear reactions involving not only heavy particles, but also γ-ray quanta. The energy of the emitted quanta has to be taken into account in the energy balance.

c) The annihilation process between a positive and a negative electron that meet. The total energy of the particles is here radiated in the form of two high-energy quanta hf, according to the reaction:

$$_{-1}e^0 + {}_1e^0 \rightarrow hf + hf$$

Both the energy law and the momentum law are violated in those nuclear processes in which negative or positive electrons are emitted (β-decay). In the β-decay a nucleus of well-defined mass M changes into a nucleus of well-defined mass $(M - \Delta M)$ under emission of an electron of mass m_0. The total loss in mass is $(\Delta M - m_0)$ and consequently one would expect that the electron would be emitted with an energy $(\Delta M - m_0)c^2$. In contrast one finds that the electrons are emitted with a continuous energy distribution involving a maximum energy E_{MAX} such that:

$$(\Delta M - m_0)c^2 = E_{MAX}$$

Apparently energy disappears for all those electrons that are not emitted with the maximum energy.

In addition, the law of conservation of angular momentum is violated. The observed difference between the angular momentum of the original (parent) nucleus and the final (daughter) nucleus is such that it cannot be accounted for by the emission on an electron only. Angular momentum must be carried away in another form.

It was therefore postulated that the excess energy and momentum were carried away by a *neutrino,* a hypothetical particle of zero (or very small) rest mass that had almost negligible interaction with matter, so that it would be extremely difficult to detect. It must be considered as a sign of great experimental skill that this elusive particle has indeed been identified in recent experiments.

The condition for stability against positive or negative electron emission is that E_{MAX} is less than zero or ΔM less than m_0. A condition for stability against orbital electron capture can be given in a similar manner*. With the help of these criteria it is possible to decide whether or not a given nucleus is stable. Roughly speaking, a nucleus will emit negative electrons if it contains too many neutrons; it will emit positive electrons if it has a defect of neutrons. The processes will continue until stable isobars are reached in each case.

The forces between the particles inside the nucleus are of two types, a general short-range attraction between the constituents and electrical repulsion between the protons. If one goes to heavier and heavier nuclei, the most stable configuration must contain more and more neutrons to overcome the electric

---

*Textbooks usually give the above condition, not in terms of the *nuclear* masses, but in terms of the *atomic* masses. It is not difficult to change from the one presentation to the other.

repulsion between the protons. Finally, the nucleus contains so many protons and neutrons that it becomes energetically favorable to shed part of its constituents. This is the reason why practically all elements above lead (Z larger than 82) are unstable against α-decay or β-decay or both. Most of these elements can be arranged into three sequences of α- and β-decays starting with the long-living nuclei $_{90}Th^{232}$ (thorium) and the two uranium isotopes $_{92}U^{235}$ and $_{92}U^{238}$, respectively, and ending up in stable isotopes of lead. This knowledge is used in radioactive dating methods (see Chapter 12).

Above uranium (Z larger than 92) the half life of the nuclei (that is the time during which half the nuclei decay) is much smaller than the age of the earth (about four billion years), so that any that might have been present originally have long since disappeared. Only the three long-living nuclei just mentioned have half lives comparable to the age of the earth and for that reason an appreciable number are still present. Many transuranic elements (up to and above $Z = 100$) have been found, and one of them, plutonium $_{94}Pu^{239}$, plays an important part in atomic power generation and in atomic bombs. (Chapter 11).

3. Fission and fusion[1].

If the masses of the heavier nuclei, such as $_{92}U^{235}$, $_{92}U^{238}$, etc., are compared with the lighter ones, it is found that large amounts of energy could be gained by breaking up the nucleus into two parts. Why do not these elements break up instantaneously and spontaneously? The reason is that before *breakup* or *fission* can occur, one has to deform the nucleus. A considerable amount of energy is needed to produce this deformation and, as a consequence, spontaneous fission is a rare event of negligible practical importance*.

In two uranium isotopes ($_{92}U^{233}$ and $_{92}U^{235}$) and in the plutonium isotope $_{94}Pu^{239}$ the energy supplied by captured slow neutrons produces sufficient deformation to cause fission (slow neutron fission). In the uranium isotope $_{92}U^{238}$ and the thorium isotope $_{90}Th^{232}$ fast neutrons are needed to produce fission. In most of the other heavy nuclei, especially below $Z = 82$ (lead) the neutron energy needed for producing fission is much larger than the neutron energies commonly available from other nuclear reactions. Such nuclei are thus stable against neutron bombardment.

The fission process produces two nuclear fragments with a large excess of neutrons. The fragments shed them partly by emitting neutrons, but mostly by a series of electron emissions. The average number of neutrons released by a fission event is larger than unity. That makes the *chain reaction* possible that is utilized in the atomic bomb. In the chain reaction one initial neutron produces more than one neutron in the fission process that it initiates, and these secondary neutrons produce still more neutrons causing more fission events, etc. As a consequence, an ever-growing avalanche of neutrons, accompanied by fission events, is formed, which, in turn, leads to the tremendous release of energy that initiates and accompanies the explosion. Most of the neutrons are emitted practically instantaneously, but a small part of the neutrons are slightly delayed with respect to the main body of neutrons. This makes control of the fission process possible. The nuclear reactors producing power on a commercial basis make use of such a controlled fission process.

---

*Spontaneous fission has been observed in $_{92}U^{238}$. If this were the only mode of decay of this nuclear species, its half life would be 10^{16} years!

The fission process thus produces many radioactive nuclei, some of very short half life and others of much longer half life. The radiation emitted consists of β-radiation (high-speed electrons) and γ-radiation (high-energy quanta). The radioactivity of very short half life produces the powerful bursts of β- and γ-radiation accompanying nuclear explosions. The radioactivity of very long half life is responsible for the radioactive waste produced in nuclear power reactors and for the radioactive "fall-out" following nuclear explosions. (Chapter 12).

As mentioned already, the uranium isotope $_{92}U^{235}$ and the plutonium isotope $_{94}Pu^{239}$ can undergo fission upon slow neutron bombardment. In the first case it is necessary to separate the uranium isotope $_{92}U^{238}$ from the wanted isotope $_{92}U^{235}$, which occurs with a relative abundance of only 0.72%. The separation is difficult, but several methods have been developed that carry it out on a large-scale basis.

The plutonium isotope $_{94}Pu^{239}$ is obtained on a large-scale basis by bombarding the uranium isotope $_{92}U^{238}$ with relatively slow neutrons. The reactions are:

$$_{92}U^{238} + _{0}n^{1} \rightarrow _{92}U^{239};$$
$$_{92}U^{239} \rightarrow _{93}Np^{239} + _{-1}e^{0};$$
$$_{93}Np^{239} \rightarrow _{94}Pu^{239} + _{-1}e^{0}$$

where the symbol Np stands for the element Neptunium $(Z = 93)$. The reaction is achieved in a nuclear reactor consisting of bars of ordinary uranium separated by materials (known as moderators) that slow down the neutrons generated in the fission process. First some of the $_{92}U^{235}$ nuclei in the rods undergo fission. Then the moderator slows down the velocity of the generated neutrons to a level where they can either produce new fission reactions in $_{92}U^{235}$ nuclei or react with $_{92}U^{238}$ and produce $_{94}Pu^{239}$*. Since the plutonium can be separated chemically from the uranium, this process is simpler than the first one.

If one compares the masses of the light elements, one finds that large amounts of energy would be released if light nuclei could be put together to form heavier ones. This process, known as *fusion,* actually occurs in stars and in hydrogen bomb explosions. It occurs only at temperatures of many million degrees, and for that reason one commonly speaks of *thermo-nuclear* reactions instead of fusion reactions.

The two important processes operating in stars seem to be the proton-proton cycle and the carbon cycle. Both processes transform hydrogen (H) into helium (He) at high temperatures in a series of steps that can be summed up by the reaction:

$$4_1H^1 \rightarrow {}_2He^4 + 2_1e^0$$

so that both reactions produce the same amount of energy per unit mass. The first cycle goes according to the reactions:

    a) $_1H^1 + {}_1H^1 \rightarrow {}_1H^2 + {}_1e^0$

    b) $_1H^2 + {}_1H^1 \rightarrow {}_2He^3$

    c) $_2He^3 + {}_2He^3 \rightarrow {}_2He^4 + 2_1H^1$

To obtain the two light helium nuclei ($_2He^3$) for step c), the steps a) and b) have to occur twice.

The carbon cycle makes use of the stable carbon isotope $_6C^{12}$ and goes through the intermediate step of producing the nitrogen isotopes $_7N^{13}$ and $_7N^{14}$ in subsequent steps, followed by the production of the oxygen isotope $_8O^{15}$ and of the nitrogen isotope $_7N^{15}$. The nuclei $_7N^{13}$ and $_8O^{15}$ are unstable and decay under positive electron emission. The reactions are:

    a) $_6C^{12} + {}_1H^1 \rightarrow {}_7N^{13}$; $_7N^{13} \rightarrow {}_6C^{13} + {}_1e^0$

---

*If two neutrons would be generated in the fission process, each fission event in a self-sustained reaction would generate one $_{94}Pu^{239}$ atom.

b) $_6C^{13} + _1H^1 \rightarrow _7N^{14}$
c) $_7N^{14} + _1H^1 \rightarrow _8O^{15}; \ _8O^{15} \rightarrow _7N^{15} + _1e^0$
d) $_7N^{15} + _1H^1 \rightarrow _6C^{12} + _2He^4$

To have the first reaction take place spontaneously in the laboratory, it is important to keep the gases involved at the extremely high temperature of many million degrees and to prevent the hot gas from making contact with the cool walls of the vessel containing the gas. Various methods are being studied that may help in achieving this goal. There is optimism that a controlled fusion reaction may ultimately be attained.

4. Strange particles[1].

In physics there is always a tendency at work to reduce the complexity of the theory. For example, after the theory of the nucleus became established there were only six particles. Two were heavy particles, the proton and the neutron, the building units of all nuclei. Two were light, charged particles, the negative and the positive electron. Finally there was the elusive neutrino, which theoretically should have as its counterpart the antineutrino. Now many more particles have been discovered.

Two of these, the antiproton and the antineutron were expected theoretically. The antiproton should have the same mass as the proton but opposite charge, so that the name negative proton would also be appropriate. The antineutron should have the same mass as the neutron but should have opposite magnetic properties. The proton and antiproton and also the neutron and antineutron should annihilate each other when they meet, under release of the tremendous amount of energy available in their rest mass. Consequently, "matter" and "antimatter" cannot exist simultaneously.

The antiprotons were detected and identified in 1955 after the huge particle accelerator of the Radiation Laboratory in Berkeley, California, was put in operation. It can accelerate protons to such high energies that proton-antiproton pairs can be generated upon interaction with matter. The same research group that discovered the antiproton also discovered the anti-neutron. It is generated in the near-encounter of a proton and an antiproton according to the reaction:

proton + antiproton → neutron + antineutron

In this respect the symmetry in matter is thus complete.

Besides these particles one has also found particles with masses between those of the electron and the proton and particles with masses somewhat larger than the proton. The first are known as *mesons,* of which there are many different types. The latter are known as *hyperons*; they can probably be regarded as an excited proton or neutron that subsequently emits one or more mesons upon decay, just as an excited atom emits photons.

The study of the interaction of high-speed particles was formerly only possible by studying cosmic rays, high speed particles coming from the sun and from interstellar space. Now that particle accelerators are being constructed that can give particles of higher and higher energies, it becomes possible to obtain laboratory sources of antiprotons, mesons and other strange particles. The study of these particles is carried out for learning more about their properties. It is hoped that this may give one of the main clues to the constitution of matter. It is still far too early to decide whether this study will have practical applications.

REFERENCES:
[1]S. Glasstone, *Sourcebook of Atomic Energy,* l.c. (gives an excellent and simple account of nuclear physics)

CHAPTER ELEVEN

Peaceful and Military
Uses of Atomic Energy

1. Use of radioactive isotopes[1].

One of the oldest applications of radioactive materials is in radiation therapy: destroying undesirable (cancerous) growth with the help of γ-radiation. In the early days radium (half life 1620 years) was one of the most powerful sources of radiation. Lately radioactive cobalt, Co^{60}, has substituted radium because it is much cheaper, has a much smaller half life (5.3 years), and thus gives a much larger amount of radiation per unit weight than radium. It can be made by irradiating Co^{59} with slow neutrons in a nuclear reactor. Another interesting compound is a radioactive isotope of cesium, Cs^{137}. It is one of the fission products occurring in the waste of nuclear reactors. Extraction of this isotope from the waste would in addition help in solving the problem of waste disposal.

Another interesting application of radioactive isotopes is its use for tracing elements through the body and finding whether they are preferentially absorbed at certain locations. With the help of radioactive iodine I^{131} (8.05 days half life) one can study the functioning of the thyroid gland. Radioactive sodium, Na^{24}, is used to diagnose cases of restricted circulation of the blood. The radioactive iron isotope, Fe^{59}, has been used in studies of blood. Radioactive carbon, $_6C^{14}$, has been used in the study of photosynthesis in plants. In all these examples the material can be traced by its radioactivity.

In other cases non-radioactive isotopes are used as tracer elements. Here the isotope can be traced by the fact that its weight differs from that of normal atoms. The distribution of the isotope can be detected by taking samples and determining the concentration of the isotope with the help of mass-spectrographical methods. For example, the stable nitrogen isotope, $_7N^{15}$, has been used in studies of blood. The oxygen isotope, $_8O^{18}$, and the heavy isotope of hydrogen, $_1H^2$, have been used in studies of photosynthesis. Many more examples could be given. We refer here to the literature on the subject.

Radioactive materials have also been used in determining the age of minerals. We will return to this problem in chapter 12.

2. Atomic energy and atomic bombs[1-2].

One of the main peaceful applications of nuclear energy will be in the generation of power. The amount of energy released in the complete fission of 1 gram of $_{92}U^{235}$ or $_{94}Pu^{239}$ is equivalent to the heat of combustion of 3 tons of coal or 700 gallons of fuel oil. The energy that can be obtained from one pound of heavy water* by fusion reactions would be equivalent to that from 2500 tons of coal. These examples show the much larger order of magnitude of nuclear energy as compared with chemical energy.

---

*In 1957 the U. S. Atomic Energy Commission was selling heavy water at the price of $28 per pound. If nuclear fusion processes could be accomplished, this would be a very cheap fuel. Heavy water is water in which all normal hydrogen nuclei, $_1H^1$, have been replaced by the heavy isotope, $_1H^2$.

At present electric power generation from fission processes is quite feasible and several power plants based on this principle are in operation. The cost per Kilowatt hour is higher than that for electric power generated from burning coal, but it is to be expected that the cost will go down when more and better plants are put in operation. The use of power from fission processes offers great advantages in remote areas where the transportation of coal would cause difficulties.

Unfortunately the amount of fissionable material is not very large and the amount of power available from it might not last many centuries. The situation is much more promising in the case of fusion reactions. It has been estimated that if all the heavy hydrogen ($_1H^2$) available in sea water could be extracted and used for power generation by means of the fusion process, the amount of energy from this source alone would be more than one million times the energy available from all fission reactions together. This explains the tremendous interest in the fusion process. Its successful realization may be many years off, however.

In nuclear reactors a controlled chain reaction by slow neutrons is taking place. If the reactor would go out of control, the increase in temperature would be relatively slow so that only a relatively minor, though dangerous, explosion would take place. This would break the reactor apart and cause the chain reaction to stop, so that the explosion would be minor in comparison with the explosion occurring in an actual bomb.

In an atomic bomb, however, one wants a sudden release of a tremendous amount of energy so that the chain reaction is completed before the parts of the bomb can fly apart in the explosion. Starting the chain reaction in an atomic bomb is not difficult, since there are a sufficient number of slow stray neutrons in the atmosphere that can initiate it. To make the chain reaction build up rapidly, the average number of secondary neutrons, produced per primary neutron and available for further fission events, should be considerably above unity. This can only be achieved for relatively pure uranium-235 or plutonium-239 samples whose dimensions exceed a certain critical size.

In impure samples the neutrons may disappear because they are captured by the nuclei of the impurity atoms and so become unavailable for further fission events. If the size of the uranium or plutonium mass is too small, so many neutrons escape that the average number of neutrons available for further fission events is less than unity. There is therefore a critical size of the bomb. In addition, fission must, as far as possible, be caused by fast neutrons, so that the process takes place with extreme rapidity. By minimizing the possibilities of non-fission capture and making the mass larger than critical, virtually all the neutrons produced in the fission process will cause further fission.

Before the explosion is to take place, the fissionable material must have such a form that no chain reaction can be sustained. To cause an explosion, the material must be made super-critical within a very short interval of time. This may be achieved in various ways. In one of these ways two or more pieces of fissionable material, each less than the critical mass, are brought together very rapidly to a single piece that exceeds the critical mass. The energy liberated by the complete fission of 1 kilogram of uranium -235 is roughly equivalent to the energy released in the explosion of 20,000 tons of T.N.T.

The nuclear fission bombs exploded over Hiroshima and Nagasaki released an energy equivalent to about 20,000 tons of T.N.T. Since that time the design of atomic weapons has been further developed, and fission bombs with twenty-five times higher energy yield have been produced. At the same time much smaller atomic bombs have been developed for tactical support of ground troops.

The fission process releases considerable amounts of radio-active isotopes. The radioactive debris coming down to earth after an atomic explosion has taken place is the cause of the *radioactive fall-out*. The short-lived radioactive isotopes are responsible for the radioactive damage immediately after the explosion. The long-living radioactive isotopes such as Sr^{90} and Cs^{137} are responsible for the long-lasting after-effects. The amount of fall-out is proportional to the amount of uranium available in the bomb. The larger the bomb, the more serious the fall-out problem.

The temperature accompanying the explosion of an atomic bomb is believed to be about 10 million degrees centigrade, not very different from that in the interior of the sun. Consequently, the fission products, as well as any unchanged uranium or plutonium, are converted into gases at very high pressure. This is responsible for the tremendous blast causing most of the damage. In addition, the high temperature results in strong emission of thermal radiation, which is capable of causing skin burns and fires at considerable distances. Finally, the blast is accompanied by strong γ-radiation, which will cause death for exposure above a certain critical limit.

The high temperature accompanying the explosion of a fission-type bomb is sufficient to initiate thermonuclear reactions. By combining with an ordinary bomb a quantity of deuterium ($_1H^2$) or tritium ($_1H^3$) or a mixture of these with other light elements, it has been possible to initiate thermonuclear reactions between these light nuclei and thus boost the power of the explosion. This fission-fusion process is the basis of the true hydrogen bomb. Such bombs should not have much more radioactive fall-out than that developed by the fission bomb initiating the thermonuclear explosion.

A third type of bomb of even greater devastating power is based on the fission-fusion-fission process. In this superbomb the explosive power is boosted further by surrounding a hydrogen bomb with a jacket of uranium -238; the thermonuclear explosion of the hydrogen bomb produces a sufficient number of fast neutrons that allow the U-238 jacket to undergo fission by means of the fast neutron process. The added explosive power is obtained very cheaply, but the fall-out accompanying the explosion is considerably larger than for the ordinary hydrogen bomb, since so much more fissionable material is present. The fission-fusion-fission type bomb is thus a "dirty" bomb whereas the fission-fusion type bomb is a relatively "clean" bomb.

The first U. S. superbomb was exploded in March, 1954, but its secret was not revealed officially until May, 1959. This is a good example of unnecessary secrecy. The Russians knew the secret, since they had exploded superbombs earlier. Japanese scientists, not bound by security regulations, had concluded from fall-out studies that uranium -238 had been used*. The only people that were left uninformed was the general public.

The possible use of atomic bombs in a future war has overshadowed the peaceful applications of atomic energy. Even the bombs themselves might not necessarily be applied for destroying human lives, however. They might also be used as a more

---

*The proof was in the presence of the Uranium -237 isotope in the fall-out. It could only be present because of the interaction of U-238 with fast neutrons.

powerful type of explosive in certain types of mining operations. Since the explosion would be underground, there would be no health hazards involved in their use. In addition, if it were possible to develop really "clean" atomic bombs, that is, bombs whose power is mainly derived from the fusion process, it might be possible to use them for above-ground operations, such as building harbors in areas that are not too densely populated. This should not be forgotten in the discussions on banning atomic bombs.

3. Banning of atomic bombs and atomic test explosions[3-4].

We now turn to the questions: Can the use of atomic bombs be banned and the existing stockpiles of bombs be destroyed? Should the test explosions of atomic bombs be prohibited?

Let us look at the last problem first. Test explosions of atomic bombs above ground are undesirable, since they produce radioactive fall-out. The magnitude of the danger is unknown; there are pessimistic estimates, optimistic estimates, and wrong estimates. The most reliable estimates seem to indicate that the danger is relatively small but not fully negligible at present. One of the most dangerous isotopes occurring in radioactive fall-out is the long-living radioactive strontium isotope Sr^{90}. It can get into wheat and milk in considerable quantities and—because of its similarity to calcium, it is preferentially absorbed in the bones. Since not enough knowledge is presently available, it seems better to be too cautious than not cautious enough. The number of fall-out producing explosions should therefore be restricted as much as possible and further tests should be made either underground or sufficiently far outside the earth's atmosphere. It would seem that an international agreement on this *limited* problem would be feasible and that control of possible violations should be possible.

Some people would like to go further and ban test explosions altogether. If the argument is granted that atomic bombs are evil and that all preparations for atomic war should be stopped, then this would be a logical second step. It should be understood, however, that this problem is of a much wider scope than the previous one and that an international agreement on an absolute test ban, including underground tests*, is much less easily obtainable and much more difficult to enforce than the first. These two steps are often confused in discussions about the atomic bomb. The confusion even seems to have extended to the Geneva negotiations about the banning of test explosions, as can be judged from the wrangling over the detectability of underground tests.

One might consider one next logical step: nuclear disarmament. One can argue rightly that atomic war is so evil and destructive that even the means for waging atomic war should be destroyed. This is even more difficult to achieve than the first two. For politicians and military experts think in terms of national security and must weigh carefully how a given step in international affairs affects the balance of power between the West and the East. If the nuclear disarmament were not coupled to a general disarmament and no rigid control and enforcement of this disarmament were put into effect, then the balance of power would have shifted definitely to the East. On the one hand the Russian government objects strongly to adequate inspection and on the other hand the Western powers have to rely on a rigorous control and enforcement of the disarmament.

---

*It should be borne in mind that no health hazards are involved even if the possessors of atomic bombs carried out many *underground* test explosions per year.

It is difficult to see how these two radically opposed attitudes can form a basis for agreement.

One might consider one further step: unilateral nuclear disarmament. It is difficult to see how any responsible government could put this into effect. It might be possible that a smaller country, not yet in possession of the atomic bomb, might voluntarily forego the development of its own atomic bombs and rely upon stronger allies for protection. It is interesting to note, however, that there is considerable discussion in neutral countries like Switzerland about the desirability of having atomic weapons, just because they want to remain neutral and not align themselves with one of the major powers.

To sum it up, we conclude:

a) It seems possible to take adequate steps that will prevent further radioactive contamination of the earth's atmosphere and soil during peacetime.

b) It seems likely that the atomic bomb and its threat will be with us as long as the world is divided into two opposing camps with a deep mistrust for each other's aims and actions.

Will a major conflict be avoided? Nobody knows. That the major powers sometimes warn each other that certain courses of action will lead to an all-out conflict, is understandable and perhaps even beneficial. Many previous wars were fought because those that took the first steps were not fully aware of the consequences of their actions. That the major powers sometimes brag about their atomic might is disquieting. That the head of a government goes around threatening other countries with atomic annihilation is irresponsible and outright frightening.

The stand taken by the major powers seems to be that the best way to prevent an atomic war from ever happening is to be prepared for its eventuality. This was the stand taken by military leaders in the past: "To preserve peace, prepare for war." Preparation for the calamity of an atomic conflict implies developing means for sheltering the civilian population. The steps that have been taken for civil defense up to now seem woefully inadequate. If the possibility of an all-out atomic conflict is taken seriously, a much greater effort toward an adequate civilian defense will be necessary.

Is the threat to use atomic force real or is it just a threat? The country making the threat may just be bluffing and hope that by bluffing it will achieve its goal. Many Russian actions probably fall into this category. But it may also be that the country making the threat is in dead earnest and will carry it out when challenged. Nobody knows which of the two possibilities will occur in a given case. To find out, the country being threatened must be prepared to go to the brink of war. One of the chief dangers of the present situation lies in the fact that when it has been found out whether it was bluff or determination, it may be too late to change the course of events.

4. Moral and theological consequences[3-4-5].

The development of the atomic bomb marks the first time that physicists have been faced with the moral consequences of their work. In previous cases they could avoid facing it, but here such an attitude is impossible.

Some of the discussions among the scientists responsible for the development of the first atomic bombs in the U.S.A. in 1945 have been made public in one form or another. They indicate that these people were well aware of their responsibility. They also indicate how new the situation was to many of them. This has been repeated at a later date all over the world[5].

Some scientists, notably Kapitza in Russia, and some Ger-

man scientists around von Weizsäcker, have refused to contribute in any way to the development of atomic bombs[3]. This is
an honest stand that should be respected; nobody should be
forced to decide against his conscience. It is also a courageous
stand, especially for a man like Kapitza, since anybody that
takes it, casts upon himself the suspicion of lack of patriotism.
Finally, it is an uncompromising stand, for it is based upon the
conviction that there are limits beyond which one does not
want to go and that this limit has been reached here (von
Weizsäcker).

Many have taken a different stand. During the second world
war many U.S. scientists, probably more or less reluctantly in
many cases, decided in favor of atomic bomb development for
fear that Germany might develop one earlier. Later they favored
using the bomb against Japan to shorten the war and to reduce
the number of casualties. When the cold war developed, many
decided to help keeping up and extending the U.S. atomic
arsenal for fear that large parts of the free world might otherwise be dominated by the Soviets. It is the stand that the author
would take if he were called upon to make the decision; this is
strongly influenced by wartime experiences in Occupied Europe.
Everybody hopes that the need for using atomic bombs will
never arise, but many feel that the best way to prevent this
calamity from happening is to prepare for its possibility.

This, too, is an honest stand, for the dangers that are en-
visaged here are real, even though they may never materialize.
The fear for German atomic bomb development was a real
one, as is shown by the fact that U. S. field intelligence parties
tried immediately to get all the possible information on the
subject from any newly liberated European territory. That it
turned out to be unfounded at the end is another matter. Also,

the estimates about the number of casualties that would have been suffered during an attack upon the Japanese main islands are probably correct. Finally, it is probably also correct that the fear for atomic war has prevented the cold war from developing into a hot one. The stand just taken thus has political wisdom on its side. It also has the advantage that it recognizes in what kind of world we live, a world not of peace, good will and justice, but often of war, ill will and injustice.

Nevertheless, it is also a dangerous stand. The danger is that one goes farther and farther, step by step, without ever coming to the point where one must refuse and stop. In this respect those who take an uncompromising stand perform a real service to those who cannot follow their decision, for it reminds the latter of the fact that there *are* real limitations for them.

It has often been said at the beginning of a war: "We shall defend ourselves with *all* the means that are at our disposal." This ignores the fact that there *are* limits beyond which one cannot go. If this fact is not born in mind at all times, a deterioration of our standards becomes unavoidable. That our standards have, in fact, deteriorated during the last fifty years becomes apparent when one observes how our concepts about permissible and nonpermissible acts of war have changed during that time.

There can be real limitations of our duty to defend the country. Pope Pius XII said on October 19, 1953 in a speech for military medical officers about atomic war: "If the damage that the war brings along is out of proportion to the injustice that one has to suffer, it may be our duty to submit to this injustice." Does this mean then that we should follow Bertrand Russell's advice and surrender to the Soviet leaders rather than fight an atomic war? Of course, no responsible government could do that, for fear that the Soviet leaders would quickly seize the opportunity and threaten everybody into subjection. One should, however, be aware of the fact that it might under certain circumstances be advisable to suffer injustice.

In 1957 the deans of the six theological faculties in East Germany had this to say about atomic weapons: "In ihnen werden Gottes Gaben, der menschliche Verstand wie die Kräfte der Natur misbraucht. In ihnen wird der Mensch, der Gottes Ebenbild ist und für den Christus gestorben und auferstanden ist, verraten. In ihnen wird die Güte des Schöpfers selbst gelästert."* It is easy to say that this is part of the Communist peace propaganda, though this is either not true at all or only true to a very limited extent. However, it is hard to deny the truth of what is said. It holds not only for atomic weapons, but also for other instruments of modern warfare.

Does this mean that we should abandon these weapons altogether? Indeed, that is what we *should,* there should be no war, no instruments of war and no preparation for war. The Ten Commandments declare very clearly: "Thou shalt not kill." The hard facts are, however, that there *are* wars, instruments of war of great destructive power and preparations for war. The fact that we *should* do without them does not necessarily mean that we *can* do without them. We should, however, be aware of the anomaly of the situation.

The world is caught here in the discrepancy between what *should* be done morally and what *can* be done politically. It cannot be solved by recommending everybody to quit the whole business, though it may be a prophetic act if some individuals

---

*In them God's gifts, the human intelligence and the forces of nature are misused. In them man, God's image and for whom Christ died and rose again, is betrayed. In them the goodness of the Creator Himself is blasphemed. (These quotations are taken from Gollwitzer's book).

refuse to participate. Neither can it be solved by assuring ourselves and others that everything is quite all right, since it is
obvious that everything is not quite all right. We have to face
it, live with it, and, wherever possible, try to eliminate it.

In the past the Christian churches have often tried to justify
certain wars theologically. It is to their shame that many
pacifist groups have seen the blasphemy of this attitude better
than they. The threat of atomic war has at least given the
benefit that it is no longer possible to close one's eyes for this
evil. This means that the Churches will have to revise their
thinking about war drastically.

The Christian Churches can only state that wars in general
and atomic wars in particular are against the will of God. They
should be well aware of the above discrepancy that all people
to some extent, and government leaders in particular, must
face, without trying to justify theologically the position that
the governments are taking. They should stand by those who
refuse to participate, but they should not recommend it as *the*
solution of the problem. They should understand those who
feel it as their duty to defend their country, even with atomic
weapons if the need arises, but they should avoid giving Christian blessing to this use. They should remind the leaders of
all governments to work for peace and disarmament and warn
them not to solve political problems by threat and blackmail.
And they should pray to God to grant these leaders the wisdom
and the insight necessary for finding the road to peace. Finally
they should stress that the world is in the hand of God and
that His purposes will come true despite all those who work
against Him.*

*It seems that as far as the problem of atomic war is concerned, many European theologians belong to two opposing camps, that can hardly communicate with each other. The one side, the pacifists, rejects all forms of participation, whereas the other side, the politicians, supports the Western governments theologically. What we tried to emphasize here, is that the Churches can only exercise their proper functions if they do not align themselves with either one of these two camps.

REFERENCES:

[1] S. Glasstone, *Sourcebook of Atomic Energy*, 1. c.

[2] S. Glasstone, *The Effects of Nuclear Weapons*, U. S. Printing Office, Washington, 1957.

[3] C. F. von Weizsäcker, *Die Verantwortung der Wissenschaft im Atomzeitalter*, Göttingen, 1957 (contains the declaration of 18 German atomic scientists against atomic weapons).

[4] H. Gollwitzer, *Die Christen und die Atomwaffen*, Kaiser Verlag, München, 1957.

[5] *Bulletin of the Atomic Scientists* (Periodical), has appeared since February, 1946.

CHAPTER TWELVE

Age Determinations

1. Geology and physics.

In geology one has simple means for determining the relative age of rocks. In the case of sedimentary rocks one can use the superposition principle, according to which each layer must have been deposited on top of older sediments, unless the sequence has been disturbed by the process of mountain building. This method works only over a limited geographical area, for in other areas different geological processes may have taken place. In the case of batholitic rocks that have intruded into sedimentary layers one can often find the relative date of this intrusion by determining how far the intrusion took place and what sedimentary layers show the first signs of eroded parts from the batholitic rock.

To correlate sedimentary rocks that are separated over a large distance, fossils are used. Some animals lived only over a relatively short time (relative on a geological scale, of course) and are thus characteristic for a well-defined geological period. If one thus finds these characteristic fossils in geological layers at different areas, one can be sure that these layers were deposited at about the same time.

There were at first no reliable data about absolute ages of geological samples. One can get some estimates about the age of the earth's crust by determining roughly how long it takes for mountains to erode and for sediments to be deposited. This gives values of at least 100 million years for the age of the earth's crust. It is a lower limit, for mountain building followed by erosion and deposition of sediments may have repeated itself several times. Another estimate makes use of the salt content of the oceans. Rivers bring salts to the ocean. The water of the ocean evaporates and returns to the dry land as rain, while the salts are retained in the ocean. The rain water then flows into the rivers and carries new salts from the mainland back to the ocean, which adds to the salt content already present. By dividing the amount of salt that is available *now* by what is brought in per year, one obtains an estimated age of the earth of many million years. This is again a lower limit, for a major part of the salt brought into the ocean is blown back to the mainland by the wind.

Much more reliable data became available when radioactive dating methods were developed.[1] The atomic nuclei of some isotopes of certain chemical elements are unstable and decay radioactively until finally a stable isotope of another chemical element is reached. Suppose the geological layer, when deposited, contained some of these radioactive elements. Then the age of the layer can be calculated if the half lives of the unstable isotopes are known and the amounts of the unstable and the stable isotopes present in the sample have been determined.*

If the earth's crust is really as old as the geologists estimated, then one would have to use radioactive nuclei with very long half life, since all nuclei with a short half life would have disappeared long ago. There are several suitable radioactive isotopes available[1]:

1.   The Uranium isotope $_{92}U^{238}$, with a half life of 4.51 billion years. It decays into the stable lead isotope $_{82}Pb^{206}$ in a series of steps involving only nuclei of relatively short half life.

2.   The Uranium isotope $_{92}U^{235}$, with a half life of 0.713 billion years. It decays into the stable lead isotope $_{82}Pb^{207}$ in a series of steps involving only nuclei of relatively short half life.

3.   The Thorium isotope $_{90}Th^{232}$, with a half life of 13.9 billion years. It decays into the stable lead isotope $_{82}Pb^{208}$ in a series of steps involving only nuclei of relatively short half life.

4.   The Rubidium isotope $_{37}Rb^{87}$, with a half life of 50 billion years. It decays into the stable strontium isotope $_{38}Sr^{87}$.

5.   The Potassium isotope $_{19}K^{40}$, with a half life of 1.9 billion years. It decays into the stable calcium isotope $_{20}Ca^{40}$ by β-emission and into the stable argon isotope $_{18}A^{40}$ by capturing one of the electrons moving around the nucleus (electron capture). The rate of electron capture is 12.1% of the rate of β-emission. Since potassium and calcium often occur together, it is better to use the argon isotope for age determinations.

The calculation of the age of a certain mineral is easy, once the necessary corrections have been made for the concen-

*The law of radioactive decay is as follows. Let the nuclei of an unstable isotope of an element X with a half life of 1 billion years decay into stable nuclei of an element Y, then half of the unstable nuclei will be present after 1 billion years, one quarter after 2 billion years, one eighth after 3 billion years, etc. The number of stable nuclei of the isotope of the element Y will increase correspondingly. By measuring the amounts of the isotope of element X and of the isotope of element Y, one can thus determine the age of the sample.

tration of the stable daughter product at the time of formation. In the case of the uranium and thorium methods this is possible, since one of the lead isotopes ($_{82}Pb^{204}$) is not the result of radioactive decay. In the case of the rubidium method the problem is not so difficult either since $_{38}Sr^{87}$ is not the most common isotope. In the potassium method one must determine how much $_{18}A^{40}$ was present in the sample originally.

The age determinations are based on the following assumptions:

a) There have been no gains or losses of parent or daughter elements since the formation of the mineral except by decay.
b) There have been no gains or losses of intermediate members of the radioactive decay system except by decay.
c) Proper corrections have been made for the initial concentrations of the daughter product.

Long tables of the ages of minerals obtained by the various methods have been published by Aldrich and Wetherill. The agreement in properly chosen materials is so striking that there can be no doubt that these age determinations are essentially correct. The oldest minerals tested were found to be about three billion years old.

It seems that the rubidium and the potassium methods give the most reliable age determinations. A comparison of the two uranium methods ($_{92}U^{238} \rightarrow {}_{82}Pb^{206}$ and $_{92}U^{235} \rightarrow {}_{82}Pb^{207}$) gives good agreement in some materials but poor agreement in others. This is not disturbing. In fact, such discrepancies may reveal something about the geological history of the minerals. Methods have been worked out to deduce from the observations the date(s) of the disturbance(s) that caused the discrepancy.

The above methods give reasonably accurate data for older

minerals but become less accurate for minerals less than ten million years old. For the more recent geological history one can make use of the carbon-14 method discussed in the next section or of the ionium method to be discussed below. The largest uncertainties exist in the mineral ages between 50,000 years and 10 million years, but this gap will probably be closed by further improvements of the technique.

These improvements will come from short-living radioactive isotopes. There are some good possibilities that need further exploration. One of these possibilities is to use the ionium method. Ionium is a thorium isotope ($_{90}Th^{230}$) with a half life of 83,000 years that concentrates in the sediments deposited on ocean bottoms. It has been used for studying sedimentation rates and for calibrating the carbon-14 method for older samples.

It is also possible to estimate the age of the earth in this manner. It is obvious that the earth cannot have existed for an infinitely long time. Otherwise, all radioactive elements would have decayed. Originally then, there must have been a particular concentration of the lead -204, -206, -207 and -208 isotopes. Since lead -204 is not the result of a radioactive decay, its concentration will have remained constant in time. The concentrations of the other isotopes would have gradually increased because of the radioactive decay of thorium and uranium. The later a lead sample is taken out of the (molten) interior of the earth, the richer it will be in the last three lead isotopes. If one now measures a large number of lead samples, one can extrapolate the measured concentrations to the time that they were all equal. This corresponds to the age of the earth. The first calculation gave a most probable age of 3.35 billion years with a relatively small margin of error. Later estimates, using more and better samples, give about 4.5 billion years with a more realistic estimate of the margin of error.

2. The carbon-14 method[2].

Carbon -14 (radiocarbon) is a radioactive isotope of carbon with a half life of about 5500 years. It is formed in the earth's atmosphere by the reaction of the common nitrogen isotope $_7N^{14}$ with neutrons from cosmic rays:

$$_0n^1 + {_7N^{14}} \rightarrow {_6C^{14}} + {_1H^1}$$

The relatively short half life makes radiocarbon suitable for determining the age of relatively young (say less than 50,000-70,000 years) carbon-containing samples if the following conditions are met:

1) The total amount of carbon -14 in the so-called *dynamic reservoir* consisting of the atmosphere, the seas and the living material is constant with time. This is the case if the cosmic ray flux is constant with time.

2) The radiocarbon concentration of a particular sample when it was alive is the same as that of today's dynamic reservoir.

3) During the years since the sample has been withdrawn from the dynamic reservoir, there has been no alteration of its isotopic carbon composition except by radioactive disintegration according to the process:

$$_6C^{14} \rightarrow {_7N^{14}} + {_{-1}e^0}$$

These conditions can be tested as follows:

a) By checking the uniformity of the dynamic reservoir for different parts of the world.

b) By checking samples of known age (either historic samples or wood from trees in which the tree rings can be counted).

c) By checking stratographic sequences and by comparing contemporaneous samples of different nature (e.g. wood and shells).

All these checks affirm to a considerable extent the above assumptions for good samples. Older samples buried under ground may be contaminated with carbon from younger roots of trees and plants. The measured age is then too short.

If the sample is too old, the small amount of carbon -14 left cannot be distinguished against the radioactive background measured by the equipment. For samples in which the carbon -14 content has not been enriched by thermal diffusion methods this limit lies at about 40,000 years. If enrichment methods have been used it is possible to push the maximum detectable age considerably beyond this limit. Samples having ages between 50,000 and 60,000 years have been measured successfully during the last few years.

The carbon -14 method has been used for a great number of problems. The Dead Sea Scrolls turned out to have an age of 1917 ± 200 years, as expected[2-8]. The method has been used to date textile, wood and charcoal from Egyptian tombs, to correlate the time scale between the Babylonian and Christian calendars, to determine the end of the last ice age, etc. Also dates have been determined of charred wood from caves occupied by human beings. An age of 16,000 years was deduced for samples from the Lascaux caves in France, famed for the wall paintings of ancient animals. Ages beyond 30,000 years come from Iraq and other Middle East sites. Ages of about 8000-10,000 years come from various caves in the United States. These caves were apparently occupied by human beings at that time, as charred bones and wood fragments testify.

In general one can say that carbon dating has provided us with an interesting and generally reliable tool for determining the age of samples formed during the last 50,000 years.

3. Data obtainable from stable isotopes[3].

Several interesting results can be obtained by studying the distribution of stable isotopes in geological material. We shall give a few examples.

As a first example, consider the concentration ratio O^{18}/O^{16} of the two stable oxygen isotopes $_8O^{18}$ and $_8O^{16}$ (normal) in calcium carbonate. A living marine animal deposits calcium carbonate in its shell in equilibrium with the water in which it lives. If one measures the O^{18}/O^{16} ratio, one finds that it is appreciably larger in the solid than in the watery solution and that this ratio is temperature dependent. If the animal dies, the shell sinks to the bottom and is buried in the earth. Since its isotopic constitution does not change after that, the O^{18}/O^{16} ratio can be used to determine the temperature of the sea water in which the shell was formed. This allows us to draw conclusions about climate in the long distant past.

As a second example, consider the concentration ratio C^{13}/C^{12} of the two stable carbon isotopes $_6C^{13}$ and $_6C^{12}$ (normal). It turns out to be appreciably smaller in organic material than in minerals of non-organic origin. This allows us to determine whether very old geological samples contain carbon coming from plants or animals. Since its C^{13}/C^{12} ratio will not have changed after the plant or animal died, it is in principle possible to trace living materials back into past geological periods from which no recognizable fossil remains have been left. In this manner one has concluded that some (probably low) forms of life already existed more than one billion years ago, and that oil is of organic origin.

4. The history of life on earth. Evolution.

Now that the various geological dating methods have been

perfected during the last 50 years, it is possible to give reasonably accurate dates for the most important geological periods. The values given by the various authors agree well, indicating that the time scale is well established at present. It is thus possible to put the history of life on earth on an absolute time scale. Though it is beyond the scope of this book to give a detailed account of this history, a few important aspects will be mentioned.

The historic record of life on earth is given in the fossils found in the various geological strata. It is certain that only part of this record is known at present and that more will come to light when time goes on. Moreover, the information is by no means complete. It speaks for the ingenuity of the geologists and the biologists that often reasonably accurate deductions could be made from rather limited material. It is still an open question whether the gaps existing in the record are *real* gaps or whether they are a consequence of our incomplete knowledge, and it probably will remain so for a long time to come. This means that no convincing argument should be built on either point of view, though one should be aware of both possibilities, of course.

What is most certain about the history of life is the fossil record itself and the conclusions that can be directly drawn from it. One such conclusion is that undoubtedly a large scale development has taken place. There was a succession of various forms of animal and plant life in the different geological periods. Gradually, and in some cases apparently not so gradually, many more highly developed forms of life appeared, whereas other forms of life disappeared.

There is another set of facts: the record of all forms of animal and plant life presently available. It is studied by the field of comparative morphology. It is an even more incomplete record than the fossil one in some respects, since it gives only *one* cross-section in time of the various forms of life. In other respects it gives much more complete information than the fossil record, since it allows one to study the animal and the plant as a whole. It can thus add information that cannot be obtained from the fossil record. Portmann has used the method to stress the large gap between the modern anthropoid apes and modern man.[4]

The theory of evolution tries to tie all the facts together by interpreting this succession of the various forms of life as the result of a real kinship, as a genesis of many different forms from simpler, more basic ones. It performs all the functions that a proper theory should perform, tying together the various facts by a single concept, giving perspective to the huge body of information presently available, and directing further research. Since it is a *theory,* it is subject to the same process of verification as all other theories. In several cases a very likely sequence of successive forms could be deduced from the fossil record. In other cases, such a sequence can only be guessed at and is more or less hypothetical at present.

The *mechanisms* of evolution deal with the reasons behind the developments. Several mechanisms that can at least partly explain what happened can be given. We mention two of them: natural selection or survival of the fittest, and mutations. It is rather obvious that an animal form that can no longer meet the struggle for survival will disappear; for example, various animal species have become extinct through actions of man. Mutations that cannot meet the competition with other forms of life will never develop. It is also well known that mutations *do* occur and that they can give appreciable changes, at least within the genus. Up to here one is on a rather firm basis.

What is quite uncertain, however, is whether these mechanisms can explain *all* the facts. Some biologists express confidence that mutations can accomplish this, whereas others are extremely skeptical and think that an otherwise useful idea has here been extended far beyond its limits of applicability.

Still more speculative, though highly intriguing and sometimes quite ingenious, are the evolutionary theories of the origin of life itself. The peculiar structure of all protein molecules in living material gives an interesting clue to the origin of life and there are other facts that warrant similar not very speculative conclusions. The *theories,* however, fall in a different category. They are highly speculative, though they are sometimes proposed with great conviction.[5-9]

One of the main criticisms against the mutation mechanism is that it is hard to see how random processes like mutations can explain all the order actually observed. It is highly doubtful that the invoking of time's arrow (Chapter 5) can be of great help. To quote Portmann [5-6]: "Die umfassende Kenntnis des Baues und der Funktion der Organe im lebendigen Körper führt zur Annahme dass die Formenänderung die wir im Laufe der Erdgeschichte beobachten, durch die im Laboratorium erzeugten und auch in der wilden Natur gefundenen Mutationen nur zu einem Teil erklärt werden. Dass heisst aber zugleich, dass wir andere Faktoren am Werke vermuten, unbekannte Werkweisen die sich vorderhand unserer Beobachtung entziehen." (A. Portmann, Probleme des Lebens, pg. 110).*

---

* "The detailed knowledge of the structure and the functioning of the organs of the living body leads to the assumption that the change in the forms that we observe in the history of the earth can only be partly explained by the mutations created in the laboratory and also found in nature. This means, however, at the same time that we expect other factors to be at work, unknown processes, that are escaping our observations for the time being."

The application of the theory of evolution to anthropology may eliminate part of the problem under study. For example, if the higher mammals are used as a standard of comparison in the understanding of man, then the human spirit is ignored and man is dehumanized. As Portmann puts it: "Die heute am weitesten verbreiteten Auffassungen beziehen das biologisch Fassbare des Humanen stets auf das höhere Saugetier als Norm, und schnuren zu diesem Zwecke von vornherein das nicht Vergleichbare, das Besondere, als "Geistiges" von diesem Menschen ab. Das übergebliebene "Präparat" wird dann der Lebensforschung als ihr Objekt übergeben. Im Gegensatz zu dieser Auffassung gewinnen *wir* die entscheidende Beurteilung der menschlichen Entwicklung aus der Zuordnung zum Gesamten der menschlichen Lebensform." (A. Portmann, Biologische Fragmente zu einer Lehre vom Menschen, 2nd Edition, preface).*

These quotations from Portmann are not given to create the erroneous impression that he is opposed to the theory of evolution as such. He is, however, well aware of its uncertainties and of the limitations in its application.[4-6]

5. Conclusions.

At first, the conclusions from the past geological and biological history of the earth created considerable concern in many Christian circles, because of the apparent clash with accepted views about creation. In such cases it is important to distinguish between facts, theories, speculations and world

---

*"The views that are most widespread today always relate the part of man that can be understood biologically to the higher mammals as its standard and to that end separate from man in advance the spiritual as the incomparable, the special. The "preparation" that remains is then given to the life science as object of its study. In contrast to this view *we* obtain the decisive evaluation of the human development from the relation to the whole of the human form of life."

views. If necessary, one can adjust to facts, as Church history clearly shows. In general it is also not difficult to live with theories, especially if one understands the degree of their certainty. Finally, one can take speculations for what they are, though one should be aware of the possibility that their status may change.

Things are different if one has to do with a world view. The theory of evolution was often represented in the past as if it were more than a theory: it often took the form of a world view, a creed. In such a case opposition was certainly warranted. Opposition is also warranted where the theory ignores vital aspects of the human form of life, as was mentioned already in Portmann's criticism of the evolutionary account of human development. It is interesting to note that both orthodox and liberal theologians resisted the descendence theory of man on this ground.[7]

Before all, one should ask whether the apparent clash is real or imaginary. It is imaginary if the Christian concept of creation has been tied to scientific points of view that were discarded by responsible scientists long ago. In such a case it is necessary to remove those ties and thereby eliminate the discrepancies. That such ties did exist in the past, is not so surprising. It makes a difference, however, whether or not one is aware of their existence. This problem will be discussed in more detail in chapter 15.

REFERENCES:

[1]L. T. Aldrich and G. W. Wetherill, *Geochronology by Radioactive Decay*, Ann. Review of Nuclear Science, Vol. 8, 1958, pp. 257-298.

[2]W. F. Libby, *Radiocarbon dating*, 2d ed., Univ. of Chicago Press, 1955.

[3]K. Rankama, *Isotope Geology*, McGraw Hill Book Co., New York, London, 1954.

[4]A. Portmann, *Biologische Fragmente zu einer Lehre vom Menschen*, B. Schwabe & Co., Basel, 1951.

Reprinted as: *Zoologie und das neue Bild des Menschen*, Rowohlt, Hamburg, 1956.

[5]A. Portmann, *Probleme des Lebens*, F. Reinhardt, Basel, 1949.

[6]A. Portmann, *Vom Ursprung des Menschen*, F. Reinhardt, Basel, 1944.

[7]Karl Barth, *Kirchliche Dogmatik*, Vol. III.2 (contains references to the theological opposition against Darwinistic anthropology).

[8]Millar Burrows, *More Light On the Dead Sea Scrolls*, Viking Press, New York, 1958.

[9]A. I. Oparin, *The Origin of Life*, Dover Publications, New York, 1953.

[10]F. C. Haber, *The Age of the World, Moses to Darwin*, The Johns Hopkins Press, Baltimore, 1959 (gives early history of geological chronology).

CHAPTER THIRTEEN

The Study of The Universe

1. Distances in the universe[1-8-10].

In determining the distance to inaccessible points on earth one uses a simple geometrical method. First one measures accurately the distance between two points A and B that are chosen so that the inaccessible point C can be seen from both points. After having determined the angles between the lines AC and AB and between BA and BC, one may calculate the distances AC and CB. The greater the distance of the point C, the longer one has to take the known length AB to make an accurate distance determination.

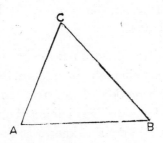

The same process applies to our solar system, but because of the large distances involved one must use two points on

earth that are relatively far apart. In that way one has determined that the moon is 239,000 miles away and the sun
93,000,000 miles. By also determining the angular diameter
of the sun and the moon it is possible to determine their linear
diameters. For the sun this turns out to be 865,000 miles.

If one wants to apply the method to determining the distances of stars, one must choose the distance AB much larger
than can be obtained for any two points on earth. Fortunately,
a much larger distance is available. Because the earth rotates
around the sun, a base length AB of 186,000,000 miles is
obtained by measuring the position of a star at two instants
that are half a year apart. The distances thus obtained are so
large that it is better to use a larger unit of distance: the light
year. Light travels with a speed of 186,000 miles per second.
A star is said to have a distance of one light year if it takes the
light one year to travel the distance.

It turns out that the nearest star is about 4.3 light years
away. The average distance between stars in our vicinity is a
few light years, so that space is almost empty. The method
ceases to give reliable results for distances larger than a few
hundred light years, since the measurement becomes inaccurate
at such large distances.

A still larger base distance AB can be obtained by studying
the motion of stars through space. Seen from our own solar
system the relative motion of the stars can be separated into
radial motion (along the line joining the sun and the star)
and the motion along the sky, known as the "proper" motion.
If the speed of the solar system is known, it is possible to measure distances with the help of a base length $AB = vt$, where v
is the velocity of the solar system and t the time between observations.

Actually, because of the motion of the stars under study, the situation is more complicated. But it remains true that distances can be determined from a detailed analysis of observations extending over many years. Distances up to 3,000 light years can be determined in this manner. The proper motion of the stars can be determined by taking photographs of the relative positions of the stars over prolonged periods. The radial motion can be determined with the help of the Doppler effect. The name "Doppler effect" refers to the dependence of the frequency f of a moving light source upon its velocity v. If the source is moving away from us, the frequency is decreased by an amount $\Delta f = f\, v/c$, where c is the velocity of light, so that all known spectral lines are then shifted toward the red. If the source is moving toward us, the frequency is increased by an amount $\Delta f = f\, v/c$ so that all known spectral lines are then shifted toward the violet.

For still larger distances one has to make use of other methods. These methods are all based upon the principle that the light intensity received from a star is inversely proportional to the square of the distance. If one knows the total amount of visible radiation emitted by a star (this is called the *absolute brightness*) and one determines how much is actually received (this is called the *relative brightness*), one can determine the distance. Unfortunately, one does not know the total amount of radiation emitted by most stars, but for certain groups, like the R.R. Lyrae group and the Cepheid variable group this is the case.

The R.R. Lyrae stars are oscillating stars. Their light emission varies periodically with a period between eight hours and about a day. Their absolute brightness is always close to 100 times that of the sun*. The Cepheid variable stars are pulsating stars in which the frequency of the light pulsation depends upon the absolute brightness. Once this dependence has been calibrated it becomes possible to use these stars for distance measurements**.

At first it was assumed that all Cepheid variables fell on the same calibration curve, but this turned out to be incorrect. There are two calibration curves, one for population I and one for population II variables. Population I stars are young, bright stars (10-100 million years old) occurring in the spiral arms of spiral galaxies, whereas population II stars are old stars (up to five billion years old) concentrated toward the center of such galaxies. Some stellar systems consisting of older stars have only population II stars and cepheid variables belonging to that group. Once this difference was known, it could be taken into account. This raised the distance scale of the universe by a factor 2.

With the help of R.R. Lyrae stars it is possible to measure distances up to about 600,000 light years. These stars have been used to measure the distance of the sun to the center of our galaxy. This gave a value of about 25,000 light years. The cepheid variable method has been successfully used for distances up to about eight million light years. This is sufficient for several nearby galaxies. The galaxy catalogued as M31 and lying in the constellation Andromeda is about 1.4 million light years away. Another galaxy catalogued as M81 is about eight million

---

*This is known from studying R. R. Lyrae stars in globular clusters of stars associated with our galaxy. These stars have all the same distance to our solar system. They also have the same *relative* brightness, so that they must also have the same *absolute* brightness.

**Cepheid variables in nearby galaxies such as the Magellanic cloud have the same distance to us, so that their relative brightness is a measure for their absolute brightness. One can now plot the frequency of the pulsation against the relative brightness. By measuring the light output of cepheid variables located in our own galaxy at a known distance from the sun, one can change this calibration curve into an absolute one.

light years away. The present distance scale of the universe cannot be too far off for distances less than 10 million light years.

By using the light from a globular cluster of stars it should be possible to extend distance measurements up to about 60 million light years and by using light from whole galaxies one is able to come much further. The difficulty is here that one does not know the absolute brightness. It is therefore assumed that the brightest galaxies have an absolute brightness equal to the Andromeda galaxy M31. Once the absolute brightness of this galaxy is known, one can measure distances with the help of the above assumptions. The results obtained can be checked by comparing the angular diameter of the galaxy with that of the Andromeda galaxy M31. It turns out that this gives reasonable agreement. The distance scale beyond 10 million light years is not as firmly established as for the smaller distances, however.

2. The structure of the universe[1-8-10].

Now that the distances are more or less fixed, it is possible to study the structure of the universe in more detail. The structure of our own solar system is well known and we can omit a discussion here. The structure of many other galaxies is known, since we can look at them from the outside. They are divided into spiral galaxies, elliptic galaxies and irregular or shapeless galaxies. For some of the nearer galaxies it has been possible to resolve the individual stars, even in their central parts. For more distant galaxies this is only possible for the stars lying outside the main body of the galaxy in the so-called spiral arms, and for still larger distances the individual stars can no longer be resolved. The number of stars in a galaxy is enormous, numbering from 100 million in the smaller galaxies up to 10 billion in the largest ones. In addition, there are gas clouds in some galaxies, especially in the spiral arms of spiral galaxies.

The structure of our own galaxy, more popularly known as the Milky Way system, is more difficult to unravel, since we form part of it and cannot look at it from the outside. It took a long time before it was fully understood that it is a spiral galaxy similar to the galaxy M31 in the constellation Andromeda. We now know that it is a flattened disk of about 60,000 light years in diameter. It has a central part with a long diameter of about 15,000 light years and a short diameter of about 6500 light years. The remaining part consists of the spiral arms. The sun is located in one of the spiral arms at a distance of about 25,000 light years from the center of the galaxy.

Outside the main disk there are globular clusters of stars distributed more or less evenly around the disk. Their concentration is largest near the central part and decreases with increasing distance. Practically none are found at a distance larger than 20,000 light years from the center. Each cluster contains about 100,000 stars. Similar clusters have been found to be associated with other galaxies. One of them, the globular galaxy M87, has about one thousand globular clusters.

The structure of luminous gas clouds can easily be observed. The structure of dark gas or dust clouds can be observed because they scatter and (or) absorb part of the light from the stars behind them. Clouds of cold hydrogen gas are now detected with the help of a new powerful tool: the study of the radiation emitted by the hydrogen atom in its ground state at the radio frequency of 1421 megacycles*. From the shift in frequency caused by the Doppler effect it is also possible to determine the radial velocity component of the gas (compare previous section).

---

*See bottom of next page.

Just as stars are grouped together in galaxies so the galaxies themselves are grouped together in supergalaxies. The supergalaxy to which our own galaxy belongs has a strongly flattened structure with a longest diameter of about 40 million light years and a shortest diameter of about eight million light years. Other supergalaxies outside our local one have also been found.

The flattened structure of the spiral galaxies and of the local supergalaxy seems to indicate rotation. It seems that the sun is rotating around the center of our galaxy with the speed of about 150 miles per second. Despite this large speed, one complete revolution will take about 200 million years, because the distances involved are so huge. There are also some indications that parts of our local supergalaxy are rotating.

3. Evolution of stars[3-6-9].

The stars in our, and in any other galaxy, fall in two classes: Type I and Type II stars. Type I stars are bright young stars, whereas Type II stars are less bright, older stars of up to five billion years old. Type II stars occur mostly in the central part of a galaxy. The spiral arms of a spiral galaxy are made up of Type I and Type II stars.

Type I stars are huge stars that emit so much radiation that they will exhaust their supply of nuclear energy in about 10-100 million years. That they are young stars follows from the fact that they have been found in expanding open clusters. By measuring the motion of the individual stars in the cluster and trac-

---

*A hydrogen atom in its ground state has two energy levels close together. The splitting arises from the magnetic interaction between the proton and the electron spinning around their respective axis. The lowest energy level has the two spins in parallel and the higher energy level has the two spins antiparallel. The radio frequency is emitted in a transition between these two energy levels.

ing the motion back into the past, one finds that they had a common origin. Setting this common origin as the beginning of the stars, gives an expansion time, and hence a lifetime, of several million years.

The expanding clusters seem to indicate that in the process of star formation a large cloud of gas condenses into a whole group of stars. It is possible that the picking up of gas and dust has contributed to the present size of the Type I stars, since gas clouds usually seem to be associated with them. It is not unlikely that star formation always occurs in this form. That the process has only been found in a few cases can be attributed to the fact that the motion of older clusters has been disturbed so much that it cannot be traced back to a common origin.

The evolution of a star through its various stages is now reasonably well understood. Spectroscopic evidence indicates that most stars consist of hydrogen and helium with traces of other elements. The amount of energy radiated during the life of a star is so huge that only nuclear sources of energy can supply it. We discussed in Chapter 10 the fusion processes that seem the most likely sources.

Since helium is formed in the fusion process, it is assumed that a star in its earliest stage of development starts as a hydrogen cloud containing other elements in small amounts. If gravitation predominates over the random motion of the atoms, the star contracts, the interior pressure builds up and the interior temperature rises because of the transformation of gravitational energy into heat. Part of the energy generated in the contraction process is radiated as thermal radiation. In other words, the star begins to shine. First, it shines dimly with a reddish color, but gradually, when the temperature in the interior become sufficiently high, it grows brighter.

If the temperature in the interior of a star rises above a few million degrees, nuclear reactions start. First the hydrogen cycle starts, and later, at higher temperatures, the carbon cycle begins. Both these cycles are self-sustaining reactions. When this stage of the development has been reached, the contraction of the star stops and the nuclear reactions provide all the energy radiated by the star. The equilibrium condition thus obtained is, with some exceptions, a stable one. If too much energy is generated inside the star then the star expands and cools down, and if not enough energy is generated inside, then the star contracts and heats up, so that the equilibrium process is self-regulating. During aging, the star burns up hydrogen into helium, leaving a core of helium behind that grows with age. The temperature of this core gradually increases with age, which is important for understanding the life history of a star.

To understand and picture the evolution process of stars one usually makes a Hertzsprung-Russell diagram. In this diagram one plots the brightness of the star, that is, the total amount of light radiated, as a function of the surface temperature. When one represents the stars by a point in this diagram, one finds that most stars lie on or near a curved line. They are said to belong to the *main sequence*. The position of a star in the main sequence is determined by its mass. The larger its mass, the higher its brightness and the higher its surface temperature. Stars with a mass much smaller than the sun have a much smaller brightness and a reddish color (red dwarfs). Stars with a mass much larger than the sun have a much larger brightness and a bluish color (blue giants).

The relation between mass, brightness and surface temperature follows from a theoretical consideration of the equilibrium condition in the star. The condition requires that the rate at which energy is used up increases rapidly with an increase in the mass of the star. This explains the fact, already mentioned, that even the nuclear energy sources can only keep the blue giants operating for 10-100 million years. We shall see that they do not even last that long because of other effects.

The evolutionary cycle of a star is easily pictured in the Hertzsprung-Russell diagram. At first the evolution follows closely the main sequence, but at an older age deviations occur. If the helium core and the outer layer of hydrogen would mix, the energy would be generated throughout the core. It may be shown that the evolutionary cycle lies then *below* the main sequence. If the helium and the hydrogen do not mix, the energy is generated in a thin skin between the helium and the hydrogen. It may be shown that the star then follows a wild path far above the main sequence for part of the time. Experimental evidence indicates that the latter case occurs. The path expected for the sun is pictured as the path ABCDEFGH.

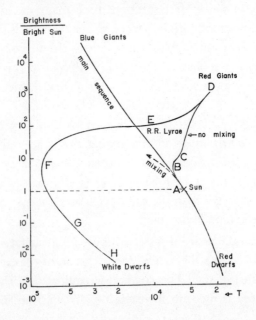

It has taken a star like the sun almost five billion years to work itself up to the point A in the diagram and it will take another five billion years before the sun will turn the corner at the point B in the diagram. After that, the evolution goes rapidly through the red giant stage at D, the R.R. Lyrae stage at E, through F and G to the white dwarf stage at H.

This is explained as follows. When the star proceeds from A to B its helium core grows and the internal temperature of the core rises. Finally, the temperature of the interior of the core becomes so high that helium nuclei can combine to form heavier nuclei such as carbon $_6C^{12}$, oxygen $_8O^{16}$, neon $_{10}Ne^{20}$, etc. This releases so much energy that the star expands rapidly to the red giant stage under formation of heavier elements*. At this stage and beyond it, the star is almost unstable. It shrinks rapidly to the R.R. Lyrae stage under a decrease in brightness accompanied by a strong increase in surface temperature. In the R.R. Lyrae stage the star oscillates in size and, as a consequence, in light intensity. After this the star rapidly contracts further to the white dwarf stage, where the density becomes as large as several tons per cubic centimeter! The surface temperature is still extremely high and, because of the small surface area, the star cools down rather slowly, so that it stays in the white dwarf stage for a long time.

The last stages between the R.R. Lyrae stage and the white dwarf stage are not without violence. When the energy-generating skin of the star reaches the surface, violent hydrogen explosions, so-called "nova-explosions" occur, leading to a large flareup in intensity for a few weeks. After the star has lost its

---

*At the point B, the temperature at the surface of the earth should be raised above the boiling point of water, whereas in the red giant stage the sun should even engulf the inner planets. The so-called "heat-death" discussed in Chapter 5 should thus be the least of our worries.

last hydrogen in a series of such explosions it settles down to its white dwarf stage.

How can one be sure that this is not a fairy tale, but is actually correct? By experimental evidence obtained by studying globular clusters. The clusters are spherical groups of rather "old" stars that are now so close together that they must have had a common origin; they should have the same age. Since they are not identical, but have different masses, they have proceeded along the evolutionary path over different lengths. Some of the heavier stars should almost have completed their cycle, whereas some of the lighter ones should hardly have started. If the theory is correct, the measured points, obtained by plotting the brightness and the surface temperature of each star in the Hertzsprung-Russell diagram, should scatter around the theoretical curve. The actual agreement between the theoretical prediction and the experimental fact is so striking that it is impossible to consider it a chance coincidence.[7-8]

Heavier stars are predicted to suffer a more violent fate. At first the helium core and then the core of heavier elements develops as in the sun. However, the temperature rises much higher, so that heavier elements, up to the iron group, are formed. All the time, enough energy is released to maintain the pressure balance, but finally, at a temperature of about four billion degrees, the dissociation of the heavier elements into helium becomes a favorable process. So much energy is required for this dissociation that the pressure balance of the star cannot be maintained and the star collapses. This causes the energy-producing outer parts to fall into the extremely hot inner parts which generates a sufficient amount of energy to release a tremendous explosion that blows large amounts of material, including heavier elements, into interstellar space.

Such an explosion is known as a "supernova" explosion. In our galaxy one such explosion occurs every few hundred years. For some supernova explosions that occurred in historic times, one has actually observed the blown-off gas cloud, expanding rapidly into interstellar space. The total estimated amount of heavy elements blown out into interstellar space by supernova explosions agrees reasonably well with the amount of interstellar matter found experimentally, so that it is fair to assume that supernova explosions are responsible for the interstellar matter.

4. The expanding universe[1-8-10].

A study of the spectra of distant galaxies indicates that the spectral lines of well-known atoms are all shifted toward the red, that is, toward lower frequencies. The larger the distance, the larger this "red shift." The most logical interpretation of this "red shift" is that it is caused by a Doppler effect. The effect then indicates that galaxies move away from us with a speed proportional to their distance. The speed with which distant galaxies move away from us is enormous. Speeds higher than 1/3 of the velocity of light have been observed.

If one now traces this recession of the galaxies back into the distant past, one comes to the conclusion that all matter must have been very close together about five billion years ago. It is interesting to note that this corresponds to about the age of the earth and of most of the older stars. It is also interesting that the meteorites (coming mainly from our own solar system) have about the same age[*]. This is the basis of a theory of the expanding universe proposed by Gamow[4].

---

[*]Earlier determinations, based upon the accumulation of helium in the meteors, gave sometimes a greater age. It turned out that this method of age determination was unreliable. The present determinations are made with the help of the rubidium and potassium methods.

This theory can be roughly presented as follows: According to it, the present universe started with a tremendous explosion in which all matter of the universe, at first concentrated in a relatively small area, expanded rapidly. The larger the initial speed of the material, the farther it has receded from the center of the explosion. During the expansion, matter first condensed into huge clouds*. These clouds formed the beginning of the present galaxies; sooner or later they condensed into individual stars.

Gamow also proposed that most of the heavier elements were formed during the early stages of the explosion. That part of the theory runs into difficulties, for it is hard to explain how the evolution of the heavier elements could ever have proceeded beyond the helium stage. It now seems more likely that the heavy elements are generated in the interior of stars and that their presence in interstellar space is caused by supernova explosions.

Where did this highly unstable initial condition come from? One honest answer would be: "We do not know, the answer to that question is outside the realm of science." Science can predict what happens *after* the initial conditions were set but it cannot discuss the "why" of these initial conditions. Another answer would be: "It could have come from an *implosion,* that is, from a motion of all the mass of the universe from infinity to the highly unstable condition just mentioned." In the latter case one has also "solved" the problem by referring the "beginning" back to an event in the infinite past about which we have no further information.

Another explanation by Bondi, Gold and Hoyle maintains

---

*It may be shown that a uniform distribution of matter is unstable in that a small initial disturbance has the tendency to grow.

that the large-scale features of the universe are the same at all points and remain the same at all times. This is known as the "perfect cosmological principle." True, the galaxies move away from us, but new hydrogen is added continuously and spontaneously so that the average density of matter in the universe remains constant. This is known as "continuous creation." There is, therefore, no "beginning" to this universe and there can be no "end," despite the violent fates of dying and exploding stars. The large-scale features of the universe remain the same at all times, and for that reason this model of the universe is known as a "steady state model."[5-6]

Which of these explanations is correct? Nobody knows, but each group, of course, defends its own theory. Time and careful experimental evidence will tell who, if any, is right. Many scientists, however, take a rather dim view of superimposing such a farflung "perfect cosmological principle" upon a subject about which so little is known at present.

Since the galaxies recede with speeds comparable to the velocity of light, the general theory of relativity must be used in the theoretical treatment of this expansion. Unfortunately, there are several relativistic models of the universe, corresponding to different geometries of the universe at large*. At present it is undecided which of these models, if any, holds, but it is possible that a decision can be made in the not too distant future. In the meantime one should be open to the possibility that the ordinary three-dimensional geometry may not hold for the universe at large.

It is beyond the scope of this book to discuss the various theories of the formation of the planets and of the moon. Brilliant as some may seem at first sight, they are to be considered

---

*On a small scale ordinary, Euclidian, three-dimensional geometry holds.

as interesting speculations. We refer to Gamow's and Hoyle's books for details about these theories.

In this case, as in previous cases, a few clear-cut facts stand out. For example, the planets and the moons in our solar system rotate practically all in the same plane. It is obvious that there must be some specific physical reason for it and that this reason is connected with the manner in which our solar system was formed.

To the layman the proposed theories of the formation of our solar system do not look as fantastic as the theory of the evolution of stars. In fact, however, the former theories are very speculative, whereas the latter is well established. It is therefore important to stress the degree of certainty of particular theories. Time and again the layman runs into surprises here.

Not all theories are equally speculative, however. One of them, an ingenious theory of the formation of the moon from a partly solidified earth, is less speculative than the others and seems to be quite plausible. In this theory, the formation of the moon is the consequence of a huge resonance tide effect, generated by the sun's attraction, in a partly solidified earth. The theory is not generally accepted, however, and we refer to Gamow's and Hoyle's books for alternate theories.

5. Conclusions.

What does one do if one tries to give a scientific description of the universe? We saw in our discussion that when the initial conditions and the laws are known one can predict what is going to happen in the future. One is here talking about a macroscopic level in comparison with which all terrestrial phenomena are small-scale. Hence, the restrictions imposed by the wave character of matter can be ignored, and a reasonable causal description should be possible. In some cases the theory, fantastic as it may seem to the layman, is well established. In other cases we neither know as yet the initial conditions nor the laws. For example, one is not yet sure about the geometry of the universe at large. Neither is one fully sure about the law of attraction between fast moving galaxies. And perhaps new ideas, such as Hoyle's idea of continuous creation, may have to be adopted if the evidence requires it.

Things may be even more difficult if the past is studied. For one can only see the end product of the process under investigation. The scientist asks the question: "From what original condition could such a situation have arisen?" The answer to this question is often not unique and consequently one finds widely different theories. In particular it is difficult to decide whether the initial condition was a *real* "beginning" or whether one can go beyond it. This was already seen in Gamow's theory of the expanding universe.

The religious description of the universe does not try to establish initial conditions, neither is it interested in physical mechanisms or physical laws. It is interested in relating the universe to God and to confess God as its Creator. This is not a scientific statement, but a statement of faith. It links the world around us to the God in Whom we trust.

REFERENCES:

[1] C. F. von Weizsäcker, *The History of Nature*, l.c.

[2] G. Gamow, *Biography of the Earth*, Mentor Books. 1948.

[3] G. Gamow, *The Birth and Death of the Sun*, Mentor Books, 1945.

[4] G. Gamow, *The Creation of the Universe*, Mentor Books, 1952.

[5] F. Hoyle, *The Nature of the Universe*, Mentor Books, 1955.

[6] F. Hoyle, *Frontiers of Astronomy*, Harper & Brothers, New York, 1955; Mentor Books, 1955.

[7] *The New Astronomy*, A Scientific American Book, Simon & Schuster.

[8]*The Universe*, A Scientific American Book, Simon & Schuster.

[9]A. G. W. Cameron, *Nuclear Astrophysics*, Ann. Rev. of Nuclear Science, Vol. 8, 1958, 299-306.

[10]G. J. Withrow, *The Structure and Nature of the Universe*, Harper Torch Books, 1959.

References 2-6 are here and there quite speculative. References 7 and 8 are popularly written but most of the papers are quite factual. Reference 9 gives the present status about what is known about nuclear reactions in stars; reference 10 gives a critical account of the various theories of the universe.

During the last few years evidence has accumulated that many stars are much older than the 5 billion years deduced from the theory of the expanding universe. Ages as high as 20 billion years have been found in some cases.

CHAPTER FOURTEEN

Science In Modern Society

1. Pure and applied science. Technology.

Pure research is research carried out to increase knowledge for knowledge's sake and not for the applications of this knowledge. The driving force is not the desire to become famous but the challenge coming from phenomena that are not yet, or at least not yet fully, understood. The reward of it is not fame, but the pleasure obtained from unraveling some of the secrets that these phenomena hold. The reason for publishing the results obtained is partly to lay claim on having discovered them, partly to help others working in the same field and partly to communicate to others the pleasure obtained from unraveling the problem.

Applied research is research carried out for the sake of ultimately applying this knowledge to *make* things. The difference between pure and applied research is that the first works for an overall general understanding of the natural phenomena, whereas applied science tries to obtain a much more detailed knowledge in specific areas. There is no sharp borderline. Two scientists may work on the same problem and obtain the same results with a completely different ultimate aim. For example, one may study the electron emission from oxide-coated cathodes either for the purpose of making better electron tubes or for obtaining a better understanding of the physical system that produces the electron emission.

Technology means developing the tools and carrying out the actual making of those things for which applied science has laid the basis. Again there is no sharp borderline. The engineers doing the actual manufacturing may run into problems that they cannot solve themselves, either because of lack of training or because of lack of time. Their job is not to do applied research but to develop and to manufacture. The help of the applied scientists is then called in to find the solution. Sometimes the manufacturing problems involved may not only give the applied scientists incentive for further research, but also pure scientists. On the other hand, the pure scientists, probing deeper and deeper into the structure of matter, have to develop and build huge accelerators that can accelerate nuclear projectiles to higher and higher energies. Many of them have to spend several years on this engineering task.

There is little sense in building a scientific hierarchy as is sometimes done. The one who tries to do so always ends up on top of the hierarchy! The difference between the various phases is not so much in the quality of the work as in the interest and motivation. As far as its impact upon our society is concerned, however, there is the following important sequence in time: pure research, applied research, advanced development, development, manufacture, sales. To maintain a healthy, growing society, an adequate emphasis should be put on every one of these items. Whether that is done is the question. Many think that not enough emphasis is put on pure and applied research in this country.

There are historic reasons for the present situation. Formerly the United States could lean on the pure and applied research done in other countries and concentrate on advanced development, development, manufacture and sales. At present, however, it becomes increasingly more important to put adequate emphasis on pure and applied research in order that the United States may maintain its present economic and military position in the world. It is therefore important that the general public learns to distinguish clearly between pure and applied research on the one hand and technology on the other hand. Such a clear distinction does not exist at present. Perhaps because of the past situation in the U.S., many think of scientific research in terms of the "hardware" that ultimately arises from it. Magazines like *Time* still discuss rockets and supersonic aircraft under the heading "science" and thus help to maintain the confusion. As long as "science" and "technology" are synonyms, it is of little comfort to know that large sums of money are spent on "science." The important question is: "How much is spent on pure and applied research?" Many estimate that this amount is not large enough, and I think that they are right.

Formerly, most of the pure and some of the applied research was done in the various science departments of the universities and at present this is still true to a considerable extent. The reason for it is that most universities offer graduate training for students aiming for the Ph.D. degree. Since one of the main requirements for this degree is the proved ability to do independent research, the universities need a sufficient staff and sufficient facilities to carry out this task. Lately more and more engineering departments of the universities have started to offer graduate training. In order to do so they had to hire more staff members to direct the pure and applied research and had to provide adequate facilities for carrying it out. As a consequence, the borderline between science and engineering has become less distinct.

At present, more and more industries start getting into pure and applied research, though this development still does not go as far as it should in some cases. The industries showing the best foresight look at their development on a long-term basis, for they know that pure and applied research form the basis upon which future growth and future earnings rest.

The last world wars have seen a strongly increased influence of modern technology upon warfare. Development of new weapons, new communication systems and new transport facilities is an ever-continuing concern of those charged with national defense planning. As a consequence, pure and applied research becomes important both for the military and for the economic security of the country. This has led in recent times to the development of large government laboratories, such as Atomic Energy Laboratories, other Government Research Laboratories and Research and Development Laboratories associated with the various branches of the Defense Department. In addition, government-sponsored research at universities and in industries has become more and more important. Some of these developments may have had undesirable side effects, but it is reasonable to assume that they will be with us for a long time to come.

2. Automatic control and storage of information.

The rapidly developing industrialization of all countries leads to ever-increasing demands for more advanced training on a wider and wider scale. This already by itself would make the ratio of unskilled to skilled laborers smaller and smaller. This will be even more true as automation develops. The more that is the case, the larger will be the demand for skill and for brains. There is a serious possibility that in the age of automation only the well-trained will be employable. It will require foresight of educators on all levels, the elementary school, the secondary school and the university level, to ensure that the students are prepared for that age when it comes.

Some fear that automation will create large-scale unemployment. But if it is properly introduced this seems unlikely. For it will not only eliminate a large number of *old* jobs but also create a perhaps even larger number of *new* jobs. The new jobs will be of a different type, however, and as a consequence the coming of automation will require a large-scale reschooling of large numbers of workers.

In modern technology a large number of jobs require monotonous and uninspiring work. On the one hand this is undesirable, since it subjects many people to work that is little more than drudgery. On the other hand it makes people with relatively little training employable. The automation of the industrial process will change this. Monotonous work will be taken over by machines and the jobs that remain will require more training, skill and creativity. On the one hand that is desirable, since it leads to jobs that are more enjoyable. On the other hand it has the undesirable feature that those who can be trained to a limited extent only may become more or less unemployable.

The industrial automation has become possible for three reasons:

a) The development of the theory of and the methods for automatic control. The principle of automatic control itself is not new, since it is employed in all living systems. What is new is that the same principle now finds large-scale application in modern technology.

b) The development of the theory of and the methods for handling and storing information. Again the process is not new. The brains of animals and man are able to handle information (response to external stimuli) and store it (memory). The genes of the living cell store the hereditary information and transmit it to the next generation. What is new is the application of these principles in industry.

c) The use of stored information for process control. Again this is in itself not new. For example, the genes of a fertilized ovum control the development of this ovum into a full-grown specimen. What is new is the application of these principles in modern technology.

The process of automation, automatic control and storage of information can also be applied to administrative processes and take most of the drudgery out of it. It can be used to control and check inventory, and be applied to the automatic processing of payrolls, to bookkeeping, data storage, data control, etc.

The development of large-scale, high-speed computers is based upon the same principles. The computing machines that are now available are non-creative and do not think, neither do they have as much memory capacity (as yet, that is) as the human brain. This is offset, however, by the fact that they carry out mathematical operations much faster than the human brain can, since they operate electronically. As a consequence, solutions of mathematical problems that would formerly have taken several years can now be obtained in a relatively short time. This has opened up the possibility of solving problems that could not be solved before by even the most skilled mathematicians.

This is of considerable importance in experimental and theoretical work. In order to check whether one has fully understood what processes are involved in a certain experiment, one must be able to give a theoretical interpretation. That is, one must be able to calculate the result of the experiment from the principles involved. The calculation checks whether all the processes involved have been taken into account correctly. The large computers allow to check this much faster than skilled mathematicians could possibly do.

If not all the processes or all the physical laws have been taken into account, the theoretical result will not agree with the experimental one. The computer then tells that something has been forgotten but it does not offer any help in finding out *what* has been forgotten. It would be of great help if machines could be developed that could help in the latter problem. Such machines would have to be able to carry out some *thinking* operations. Time will tell whether such machines can be built.

The study of automatic control and of processing and storage of information may help in obtaining a better understanding of the control and storage processes going on in living systems.

3. Moral implications.

Science and technology can be used in two ways, in the service of mankind and to the detriment of mankind. They may be used to improve health and the standard of living. They may also be used for the development of weapons of great destructive power. They may be used to relieve man from back-breaking labor and drudgery. They may also be used for his enslavement. They may be used to free man from materialistic worries and thus make it possible to pursue non-materialistic goals. But they may also become the means that drive man deeper and deeper into a materialistic outlook on life.

The evil and the good that thus becomes possible are not properties of science and technology themselves, but they are the two choices facing man. Man may choose the good, the improvement of the standard of living, the working conditions and the cultural conditions. He may also choose the evils: war, enslavement and materialism. The decisions required are not scientific decisions, not technical decisions but moral decisions. Science and technology give part of the framework in which our moral decisions have to be made but they do not supply the solution.

The question is not: "How to do it?" That is a technical question that is being solved adequately by modern technology. The main question is: "What to do with it?" and that is a moral question. It is not sufficient to appeal to the good will of all men. That is important, of course, but it is not enough, since the good will is not always present. It is easy to see the lack of good will in others; most political campaigns offer excellent examples of it. It is much less easy to see this lack in ourselves. What is needed is an acknowledgment that we are not making the moral grade ourselves, or, in other words, we must admit that *we,* and not only the others, are *sinners.*

It is hard even to see and to admit that this is the root of our troubles. Having seen it and admitted it, it is even more difficult not to look at the world with despair. It is here that the Christian message enters in. It aims at convincing us that we are sinners all right, but first of all in the sense that we are *forgiven* sinners. This means that it does not drive us into despair but revives in us the hope and makes it possible to work quietly toward the solution of the problems that face us.

I have the feeling that many of the problems facing this country, not only as far as internal affairs is concerned but also with respect to external affairs, would be easier to bear if we viewed them more in the light of the Christian message. Not because this message gives simple patented solutions. As a matter of fact, it does not. It would, however, prevent us from walking blindly into traps that are set for us, since we know what we are and also what those who oppose us are. It would also prevent us from the despair that the knowledge of the true character of our opponents carries along with it.

CHAPTER FIFTEEN

Creation

1. Science and creation[1].

It is often thought that science and the Biblical concept of creation have a considerable interrelation, since they deal with the same subject. It is hereby ignored, however, that they look at the same problem in a radically different manner. Science cannot tell us what the Christian concept of creation should be and the latter does not give us a clue to the scientific approach to the world around us. It should be clearly understood that "Creation" is a religious concept, not a scientific one.

One can explain the present condition of the universe, if one knows the initial conditions and the laws. Were these initial conditions set by God? One can say so, but it is not a scientific statement and it is not very wise theologically. For scientifically one can attribute these initial conditions to still earlier ones and this can go on to infinity, as we saw before. In other words, this God Who set these initial conditions moves away farther and farther and is occupied with less and less. The God, Whom the Christian Church confesses as the Creator, is not tied to setting initial conditions.

204

There are also people who have taken the attitude that only those things should be attributed to God that are not explainable in terms of natural causes. This attitude is even more fatal than the previous one, for it ties God's activity to man's lack of imaginative thinking. Sooner or later somebody comes along who is more clever and succeeds in finding a natural cause. Again, the God introduced in this manner moves away farther and farther and is occupied with less and less. The God Whom the Christian Church confesses as the Maintainer of the world is not tied to our lack of knowledge.

In both these attempts the position of the Christian Church would be one of fighting a continuous rear guard battle. Actually it is not the position that the Church should take. The God with which one comes into contact in this manner, or better, with which one fails to come into contact, is nothing but our own invention and a rather poor one at that. Even if one goes about the problem in a more subtle manner, one does not fare any better, since the source of knowledge about God does not lie in science. For that reason the whole enterprise should be *dropped*. One then has at least the possibility of grasping where the Christian thinking about God has its start and its basis.

When one looks at the Christian confession of God as the Creator and the Maintainer of the universe and compares it with what science has to say, one is struck by the contrast. Science links the present to a set of initial conditions from which this situation might have arisen. Confessing God as the Creator links the present *and* the past to God as the ground of their being. Once the initial conditions are set and the laws are fixed, everything goes by itself, so that there is no need for a Maintainer of the universe. Confessing God as the Maintainer of the universe, however, does not refer to mechanical problems at all, but sees the past, present and future as the object of God's love and care. From the one point of view one does not get the other point of view in sight. In other words, the view of science and of theology on the beginning and the maintaining of the universe are *complementary*. This explains Newton's difficulties (Chapter 3) where God's activity was restricted to that of an engineer and to a repairer of the world machine.

Creation is not simply "setting a beginning," either of the universe or of our existence. It gives this existence its *ground,* its *goal* and its *future.* It is sometimes argued that even though the Biblical concept of creation is much more than "setting a beginning," the latter is at least part of it. Convincing those outside the Christian Church that the universe had a beginning might then be a first step for them toward believing in God.

That the *universe* had a beginning is reasonable, though it is debated by the defenders of "continuous creation." That all matter presently encountered in the earth, the sun and the individual stars had a beginning can be proved scientifically. Can one now conclude from this that an unknown X, that one can later equate to God, created the universe? It is indeed an interesting philosophical question whether a "beginning" implies a "Creator." Whatever it does, it does not imply the God of the Old and the New Testament.

The God, Whom the Christian Church confesses as its Creator is not an unknown X, but is the God Who made Himself known to man. Creation in the sense of "beginning" does not simply mean "there was a beginning," but "God made a beginning." This is a statement of faith that cannot be proved or disposed of by science. Faith can step boldly where science, respecting its limitations, has to halt.

We saw in the case of the expanding universe that it was difficult to decide whether the initial conditions meant "scientifically" a *"real"* beginning beyond which one cannot go. The religious statement: "God made a beginning" is not in this category. Since the beginning is linked to God, it means, theologically speaking, a *real* beginning, beyond which one cannot go.

There is no discrepancy between creation and development through natural causes. When we confess God as our Creator, we do not *deny* the natural causes through which we came into being. On the contrary, we confess that *in, through* and *despite* these causes God has given our life sense and meaning and that He is the ground of our existence. No scientific investigation can lead to such a conclusion. It is a conclusion of faith.

In my opinion much of the discussion about creation is far too naturalistic. One looks for *causes* and *mechanisms* instead of looking for *relations*. The Biblical account of creation leads in a completely different direction. It does not discuss causes and mechanisms but relates the God whom we know by faith to the world around us.

Though the confession of God as Creator of heaven and earth is independent of our detailed knowledge of the world around us, we may have to extend its scope if our knowledge grows. Since the existence and the structure of the atom has been clearly established, it is religiously sound to call God the Creator of the atoms. We thereby continue the line drawn by the Bible. Nevertheless, we should be careful. As science develops, it deals not only with "things," such as animals, plants, stars, atoms, etc., but also with "concepts" useful in the systematic organization of our knowledge of nature. It would be hazardous to call God the Creator of these concepts, since it is quite clear that *we* are the inventors.

From a religious point of view all real understanding is a gift of God. But in applying this we must be careful. In the course of their work scientists introduce many useless concepts and wrong ideas that are discarded later. These wrong concepts and ideas should not be attributed to God, but are our own responsibility. Around 1900, for example, physicists believed in the existence of an all-pervading ether through which electromagnetic phenomena propagated. The pious ones among them praised the wisdom of the Lord that had created it to make these phenomena possible. A few years later the ether was discarded.

2. Harmonization efforts[6-7-9].

It has often been tried to harmonize science and the account of creation in Genesis. One is struck by the untheological, naturalistic character of the effort. It is not so surprising that many who tried so hard to harmonize put much emphasis on *natural theology,* that is, on what man can know about God outside revelation.[9]

A theologian should not look with one eye in the Bible and with the other eye in a geology or biology textbook. That will only lead to confusion. He should stick to his theological task and that is listening to the Bible and the Bible only. Harmonization links our thoughts to the wrong problems. It creates the wrong impression that the Christian message is in some ways subjected to science, whereas in fact it is independent of it.

It has often been observed approvingly that the appearance of plants and animals in Genesis 1 agrees roughly with what is known from geological evidence. If that is so, then that is quite accidental. To obtain such an agreement was apparently not one of the worries of the writer of that chapter. It should not be forgotten that it is a *religious* account and that its theological relevance is much more important than its supposed scientific relevance.

The seven days of creation are often interpreted as seven periods of creation, for "one thousand years are in God's sight as one day." And then the correspondence with geological periods is noted approvingly. It should be taken into consideration, however, that the account of Genesis 1 is built on a seven-day week culminating in the Sabbath day and that the whole theological point of the account is lost if the days are changed into periods.

Others try to put most of geology into Genesis 1:1, which states: "In the beginning God created heaven and earth." It is quite doubtful that this can be done, for many think that this first sentence is the *heading* of the Genesis account of creation. Moreover, it does not at all agree with the later parts of the Genesis account. It is better to abstain from such "clever" solutions.

Genesis 1 and 2 do not give an account of "how it all came about." Genesis 1 is not an effort to "explain" the world. That was left to the pagan cosmologies developed around Israel. Of course the Genesis account uses many ancient cosmological concepts, as should be readily admitted. But they are used to convey a very particular message and it is the *message* that is important. Genesis 1 and 2 are intimately linked to Genesis 3: the story of human sin. If that is understood then it is seen that the whole point of the first three chapters of Genesis may be missed when efforts are made to harmonize it with science.

Neither is Genesis 3 a "theory" of how evil came into the world, as some people seem to think. The Bible is "witness" and at this particular point it is witnessing of human sin and God's grace. One might paraphrase this as follows: "Hardly was man created and had received from God his existence, his goal and his destiny, or he rebelled against God by wanting to be like Him. Thereby man cut himself from the ground of his being." This is not the end of the story, however. A new chapter, that of redemption, begins.

To harmonize the account of Genesis with modern science or to "improve" the story with its help, is therefore wrong, for it eliminates important parts of the message. The story of creation should be read as is, without comparing it with or correcting it by what modern science has to say about the origin of the universe, the earth and man. Only then does one understand the beauty of the story and the powerful message that it brings.

The Bible is not interested in the age of the universe and it does not convey the idea that the world is about 6000 years old. The 6000 years stem from attempts to harmonize the Bible with early science. To see in the first chapter of Genesis a timetable of past events as Bishop Usher did, is just as wrong as seeing in the Apocalypse of St. John a timetable of future events. It imposes upon Genesis a framework that is alien to it and that hampers its understanding instead of promoting it. It is forgotten that the Bible is "witness," a witness about God, His relation to man and man's relation to Him. On the other hand it would also be impossible to incorporate the idea of a five billion year old universe or the idea of an organic evolution into the account of creation; not because these ideas have no truth in them, but since they do not fit there at all. To impose the framework of modern science upon the first chapters of Genesis, would remove its character as "witness."*

The Dutch theologian Noordmans[4] once compared the first chapters of Genesis with a Greek drama in which there is unity of place, time and action. In order to present the message of creation, the attention is focused on a limited scene: the garden of Eden, not a universe of staggering proportions. It deals with a limited time interval: six days of creation, not a duration of billions of years. It tells of a limited action: the creation of heaven and earth and of man, not an evolution of almost limitless forms of matter in the universe or an evolution of almost limitless forms of life on earth. Only against this limited background can the story of creation be told and the message be transmitted.

3. Creation as a conclusion of faith[1-3-5].

When the religious statement is made that God created "heaven and earth," as the Old Testament puts it so characteristically, it should be understood that it is not an "explanation" of the world around us. Neither is it a conclusion from what is *seen*. It is not a pre-scientific understanding of the world around us that has now been superseded by the modern scientific approach. Neither is it interested in the "origin" of the universe as so many scientific speculations are. It is a statement that does not in any way depend on further knowledge or better understanding that may be acquired in the course of time. It is a *religious* statement, a conclusion of *faith*. It relates the world that we *see* to Him that made Himself known to us.

---

*The theological meaning of the first chapters of Genesis is independent of the age of the universe. To *tie* a timetable to it is poor theology.

This is clear from both the Old and New Testament. Consider, for example, the creation accounts in Genesis 1:1 — 2:4a and Genesis 2:4b — 25. When Prof. Karl Barth discusses these chapters in Vol. III.1 of his Kirchliche Dogmatik he discusses Genesis 1:1 — 2:4a under the heading: "Die Schöpfung als äusserer Grund des Bundes" (Creation as the external basis of the covenant). Genesis 2:4b — 25 is dealt with under the heading: "Der Bund als innere Grund des Schöpfung" (The covenant as the internal basis of creation). Creation as the external basis of the covenant emphasizes that which made the covenant *possible*. The covenant as the internal basis of creation emphasizes the covenant as the *reason* for the creation. The first account culminates in the Sabbath day, the great sign and seal of the covenant between God and Israel. The second account uses the name Jahweh for God, the God of the prophets, the God of the covenant. By calling Jahweh the Creator, the writer of Genesis 2 has hereby linked creation to the covenant and by letting the first account culminate in the Sabbath the writer is doing the same thing. Creation is thus a conclusion of faith in Genesis. One might paraphrase it this way: "The God who led Israel out of bondage, revealed Himself on Mount Sinai, made His covenant, and established the Sabbath day as a sign of it, also created heaven and earth."[1]

The same is true for the New Testament. The prologue of the Gospel of St. John says: "In the beginning was the Word . . . All things were made by Him . . . and the Word was made flesh and dwelt among us." In the order of *knowledge* the primary fact is the Incarnation, the coming of Christ into the world. Only someone who has understood and believed what the Incarnation has brought can make the daring conclusion: "All things were made by Him." Only someone who has understood: "The Word was made flesh" would dare to

link it to the first chapter of Genesis, where it is repeated time
and again: "And God said . . . and it was so." Here, too, creation is a conclusion of faith. One might paraphrase it this way:
"He Who came into the world to redeem us is the same as He
Who created heaven and earth."

4. The Biblical account of Creation[1-5].

The Biblical concept of creation is developed all through
the Bible, but in particular in the first chapters of Genesis.
Any theological discussion of creation has to start there. Professor Karl Barth's volume III.1 of his "Kirchliche Dogmatik"
deals with these chapters. In the preface to that volume Barth
first discusses whether the interpretation of the first chapters
of Genesis requires a discussion of the questions raised by
science and he says: "Ich meinte das ursprünglich tun zu müssen, bis es mir klar wurde das es hinsichtlich dessen was die
heilige Schrift und die Christliche Kirche unter Gottes Schöp-
fungswerk versteht, slechterdings keine naturwissenschaftliche
Fragen, Einwände oder auch Hilfstellungen geben kann.*"
And with this he turns directly to discussing the exegetic and
dogmatic problems raised by the first chapters of Genesis.[1]

We now discuss a few aspects of the first chapters of Genesis that have been pointed out by Barth and others. First consider the seven days of creation as given by the first creation
account in Genesis 1:1 — 2:4a. It culminates in the seventh
day, the Sabbath day, in which God rested from all His works.
As the creation story puts it: "And God blessed the seventh
day and sanctified it: because that in it he had rested from all

---

*I thought initially that I had to do this, until it became clear to me that there
can simply be no questions, objections or auxiliary theorems from the natural
sciences with respect to what the holy Scriptures and the Christian Church
mean with God's work of creation.

his work which God created and made." The Sabbath day is in the Old Testament the sign and seal of God's covenant of grace. The special mention of the Sabbath day as the day on which God rested from all his work, means that the creation had one single aim: "To set the scene for God's gracious, solidary action toward man." (Wiersma)[3]. Change the seven days into seven periods and the whole meaning of this climax of the creation story is lost.

Genesis 1 states that light was created *before* the sun, moon and stars. If one understands it as a scientific statement, one has great difficulty in reconciling it with what we know about light and light sources. It is highly doubtful that it fitted with the knowledge about light and light sources existing at the time the story of Creation was first told, for the ancient concept was that the sun, moon and stars were the divine givers of light and the shapers of man's destiny. When one asks about the *religious* meaning of the statement in Genesis, one can see it as a polemic against this ancient concept. It tries to convey the idea that the sun, moon and stars are not divine, but are *fellow creatures* to whom *God* has bestowed the power to give light. They have power, but it is *derived* power. God *gave* it to them; they rule by the grace of God. It is interesting to note that the same idea is also found in the book of Revelation, where Christ is pictured as holding the seven stars (= the seven planets) in his right hand, indicating that Christ rules the world and guards His Church. To emphasize that God gave the sun, moon and stars this power in his *freedom,* and not of necessity, it is added that light was created first and that it was "hooked onto" the sun, moon and stars later. Any atempt to harmonize this story with modern science would have eliminated this message.

This passage demonstrates the anti-pagan character[5] of the Biblical witness; the sun, moon and stars are here dethroned as deities and become fellow creatures. The chaos (Gen. 1:2) about which the ancient mythologies knew so much becomes here that which was rejected by God when He said (Gen. 1:3): "Let there be light." (Barth)[1]. The end of the first Genesis account (Gen. 2:4a) reads: "These are the births of the heavens and the earth that they were created.*" The Babylonian mythologies pictured the beginning of the world as a birth. As a polemic against this the Bible states: "Their birth was that they were created." (Wiersma).[3]

The position of the Church against the world views is not something that was invented recently but is something that was the task of the Church at all times. That is what the anti-pagan character of the Old Testament and of the first Chapters of Genesis indicates. It is a witness *for* God, and against the idols and the world views associated with them. It would be wrong to ignore or eliminate this character.

It is also important to emphasize the prophetic character of Genesis**. The Bible starts with the prophetic account of Creation and of man's fall in Genesis and ends with the prophetic account of the end of time in the Apocalypse. The latter is not primarily an eyewitness account, even though it repeats time and again: "And I saw . . ." It gives witness in visionary form. The prophetic writer looks toward the end of time and

---

*The King James version treats Gen. 2:4a as belonging to Gen. 2:4b and translates: "These are the generations of the heavens and the earth when they were created . . . ." The above translation is preferred by most Old Testament scholars, who consider Gen. 2:4a the conclusion of the first Genesis account.

**The popular misconception is that a prophet predicts the *future*. One of the most important tasks of the Old Testament prophets, however, was to preach, to give witness. A prophet may as well give witness of the future as witness of the past.

sees that end as the fulfillment of all that was promised and as the coming of the reign of Christ in all its glory. In the same manner the Genesis account is "prophecy of the past." It is not an eyewitness account, but it gives witness in visionary form. The prophetic writer looks to the beginning of time and sees at the beginning God who created it all and man who sinned and rebelled against God[2]. Harmonization efforts tend to overlook this prophetic character of Genesis. Understanding it, eliminates a number of misconceptions and phantom problems right from the start.

5. Miracles.

A miracle is generally considered as something that is contrary to everyday experience. Sometimes one goes farther than this and defines a miracle as something contrary to the laws of nature. We shall make use of this definition to illustrate certain points, but in general the first definition is preferred for reasons to be discussed below. The character of the miracles in the *Bible* is that they are seen as signs of God's power. Whether or not they can be described in terms of scientific principles is thereby immaterial.

A Christian is not somebody who believes in "miracles," but one who believes in a God Who can *work* miracles. In this He distinguishes Himself from other Gods. The retired engineer of Chapter 3 did not work miracles; he retired after the world machine was switched on. The repairer of small perturbations in the world machine of the same Chapter did not do any miracles either; he merely kept things going. But the God who created heaven and earth works miracles. He is not the prisoner of his own creation and is not subjected to nature. He is the *Creator*, whereas man and nature are *creatures;* man is subjected to nature, God is not. God is not retired, He is active.

He is the *living* God, as the Bible puts it so characteristically. In times of need He comes to the rescue; if lawgivers and prophets are not enough, He comes Himself to do and to accomplish what man cannot accomplish himself, to redeem and to save mankind. The miracles of the Bible, against which some have objections, are small in comparison with the great miracle of God's revelation in Jesus Christ. It may be said that the many miracles of the New Testament demonstrate and accompany this one great miracle. They are *signs* pointing toward it.

There is no scientific issue at stake here. This is a religious problem before which a scientist, knowing his limitations, has to halt his scientific effort. The problem is not whether or not a miracle in the Bible can be described in terms of scientific principles; that is relatively irrelevant. The important question is whether or not it is seen as a sign pointing toward the great miracle of God's revelation. That decides between faith and unbelief.

If one would introduce the question of the compatibility or incompatibility of a certain miracle with scientific principles one would superimpose something upon the Biblical account that is alien to it. The Bible is *witness,* also when it speaks about miracles. These miracles *point* to something, want to *emphasize* something, and it is important to find out *where* they point to. Again, that is not a scientific question but a religious, a theological one.

If one wants to apply natural mechanisms nevertheless, one may distinguish between two types of miracles:
a) A natural mechanism is given or is possible. Examples are the passage of Israel through the Red Sea, where a strong wind made the sea dry, and the crossing of the river Jordan

during flood time, where the upper part of the river was temporarily blocked.

b) No natural mechanism is given and none seems apparent. Examples are the changing of water into wine on the wedding feast in Cana, the virgin birth, the resurrection.

The application of natural mechanisms does not illuminate the problem very much. But it points out at least that the existence of a possible mechanism does not rob the miracle of its character and its religious significance. The apparent absence of a mechanism does not necessarily imply that there was none, nor does it mean that the event could not have occurred.

It seems wiser to keep to the definition that a miracle is contrary to everyday experience and not bring the violation of scientific principles into the picture at all. For example, when somebody would tell that he had been to a wedding feast where water was changed into wine, most listeners would refuse to believe the story. Not because it goes against scientific principles but against everyday experience. When somebody would tell that he had just met a man alive who died a few weeks ago, very few people would believe it. Not because it is contrary to scientific principles but because it violates the common experience that someone who is dead, stays dead.

In a miracle everyday experience is not violated right and left but only at a certain point. Nowhere is it implied that the water that was changed into wine did not make people merry, or that Mary's pregnancy did not last nine months (C. S. Lewis).

There is another side to the Biblical miracles that makes it difficult to apply a scientific approach to them. A miracle is a *unique* event that cannot be repeated and that can only be verified to a limited extent (see below). Science deals generally with events that can be repeated and verified by others and interpreted in terms of initial conditions and laws. Even for a unique natural event, such as a supernova explosion, this is true. With the Biblical miracles the situation is different. They do not follow from the conditions surrounding them and their significance cannot be understood in terms of those conditions.

Those who argue in favor of the actual occurrence of the miracles often point to the reliability of the eyewitnesses telling it. One can equally well argue, however, that most witnesses are not very reliable after all. That is not a scientific argument, but it has common experience behind it. The only step that brings us here any farther is the step of *faith*. One must distinguish between faith and belief. One expresses belief if one says: "I cannot prove that the miracle occurred, but I believe it did." Faith is more; it connects the miracle with the God who made Himself known to man and recognizes it as a sign of God's love and God's power.

The strong interrelation between miracles and faith is clear all through the New Testament, especially in the Gospels. Miracles occur and are recognized where there is faith in Jesus and that faith is strengthened by the miracle. For those who saw the miracle and did not believe in Jesus, the miracle strengthened their unbelief*. Jesus refused several times to perform a miracle, when those who did not believe in him requested that he prove himself. In some cases it is recorded that Jesus did not do any miracles, because there was no faith.

The reason for telling about miracles in the Bible is ex-

---

*It is interesting to note how the scribes and the pharisees used the "scientific" principles of their day against Jesus: "He casts out devils through Beelzebub the chief of the devils." (Luke 11:15).

pressed in the Gospel of St. John (John 20:30-31): "Many other signs truly did Jesus in the presence of his disciples which are not written in this book. But these are written that ye might believe that Jesus is the Christ, the Son of God." The reason for telling of the miracles is thus to make the listeners and the readers recognize in Jesus the Christ, the Son of God.

It is of little help to use miracles in arguments against unbelievers. That did no good in Jesus' time and we have no reason to think that it should go better now. It may be of interest, however, to remove mental roadblocks and to make people reflect about what they mean when they say: "I do not believe in miracles." C. S. Lewis has many interesting things to say about this problem in his delightful book[8].

The main problem is not to explain miracles in terms of natural causes but to listen to their message. For those who have trouble to understand the message that a particular miracle brings it does not help very much to say: "It is in the Bible, and the Bible is true, hence the miracle occurred." In the effort of understanding the message of the miracle, its occurrence or nonoccurrence is not primarily at stake. What is at stake is its meaning. In this situation it may be helpful to start from the great miracle of the revelation of God's love and grace in Jesus Christ and to relate the particular miracle to it. This is especially the case in the New Testament. In the Old Testament the situation is somewhat different but there, too, the important point is listening to the message that the miracle brings. This is especially advisable for those people who feel shocked by the character of some of the Old Testament miracles.

This does not mean that it is irrelevant whether miracles did or did not occur. In the Bible the actual occurrence of *at least some* miracles is emphasized. The message of Easter is:

"The Lord is risen indeed"; there are no ifs and buts about it. The reason for this emphasis is that this miracle belongs directly to the center of the Christian message. For those miracles that do not fall into this category the chief emphasis should be on the message that they bring.

Many discussions about miracles never get beyond the question whether or not miracles can occur. They never get around to the problem of the message that the Biblical miracles bring. The present approach was chosen purposely to stress the latter point. This does not mean that the author considers the first question unimportant.

6. A diagram.

The problems that have been discussed here are presented in the form of a diagram that was developed at the suggestion

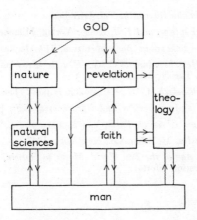

of Pastor Beisel (Fig. 5). It pictures two-way relationships, one-way relationships and lack of relationship. Man's relation to God is through faith and revelation and is in response to God's revelation to man. The road to God does not go through nature, which emphasizes that there is no natural revelation in the *positive* sense. The knowledge of nature comes through the natural sciences, but not through faith and revelation. God is recognized as the Creator of nature through faith, but the natural sciences do not lead to this confession. Theology gives a systematic account of faith and revelation but does not bypass faith as a road to God. There is no direct connection between nature and theology, which emphasizes that there is no natural theology in the positive sense.

There is no direct connection between science and theology, but there is an indirect influence through man, since the sciences influence his thinking. This may lead to a somewhat different formulation of some aspects of theology. Care should be taken that this is done in such a manner that the content remains unchanged.

REFERENCES:

[1]Karl Barth, *Kirchliche Dogmatik*, Vol. III.1 l.c.

[2]D. Bonhoeffer, *Schöpfung und Fall*, Kaiser Verlag, München.

[3]J. T. Wiersma, *De Schepping*, Boekencentrum, The Hague, 1948.

[4]O. Noordmans, *Herschepping*, N.C.S.V. (Dutch Christian Student Association), Zeist, The Netherlands, 1934.

[5]K. M. Miskotte, *Bijbelsch A.B.C.*, Callenbach, Nijkerk, The Netherlands, 1943.

[6]Otto Schuepp, *Schöpfungsbericht und Naturwissenschaft*, Reinhardt, Basel.

[7]*Modern Science and Christian Faith*, Van Kampen Press, Wheaton, Ill.

[8]C. S. Lewis, *Miracles*, McMillan Co., New York, 1947.

[9]F. C. Haber, *The Age of the The World, Moses to Darwin*, l.c. (gives account of early harmonization efforts).

CHAPTER SIXTEEN

Science and Theology

1. The hierarchy of the sciences and theology.

We have already discussed that science cannot be used as a basis for theology, since the two are independent. We also pointed out several parallels and certain differences between these two fields. Before returning to those problems it is interesting to discuss another way of linking science and theology together. In this attempt one tries to let science culminate into theology by establishing a sequence of knowledge that ends in knowing God. To that end one proceeds as follows.

If one studies the field of physics and extends it as far as possible, one comes to the properties of living material which are the domain of the biologists. Most physicists will not want to go any further, but some are interested in studying biophysics, the borderline area between the fields. Some physicists like to think that all biological phenomena ought to be described by concepts taken from physics. Most biologists, however, feel that it is a field of its own with its own laws and concepts, though they do not deny the connection.

In extending the field of biology one finally comes across

psychological problems. Most biologists do not want to go any further, but some are interested in studying the borderline areas. Some biologists like to think that all psychological phenomena should be described in biological terms. Most psychologists, however, will maintain that new ideas and concepts must be introduced to describe mental activity and human behavior, though they do not deny the links with biology.

The study of human behavior, however, leads to the problems of ethics. To study what other people do is one thing, to decide what *you should* do is quite another, for it is *your choice* and the question is: "Upon what does your choice rest?" It is certainly helpful to know the situation thoroughly and to be aware of decisions that other people made under similar circumstances, but that does not *prescribe* your choice. Concepts of right and wrong enter in.

What is needed here is something that has the power to say "You must" and that has the power to enforce it. It is here that religion enters into the picture since it determines right and wrong from the responsibility before God. And so one comes to the deepest question of all: "Is there a God and can man know Him?"

It has often been recommended by great philosophers that this hierarchy of sciences, culminating in the theological questions about God, forms the road to God. If this were the case then there would be no disharmony between science and religion but all truly scientific thinking would end in theology. It is an impressive and beautiful hierarchy, but does it indeed lead to God? We shall see that the answer is negative.

Before doing so, it should be admitted that it *might* at least have been true. Who can say that God could not have chosen this way of leading man to Him?[1] That He did not, follows from His revelation in Jesus Christ. Jesus said: "I am the way, the truth and the life; no man comes to the Father but by me." This shows the critical element of the Biblical revelation. In the first place, it means something positive: there is a road to God and those who follow it find Him. In the second place, it means something negative: there is no other road. It is not possible to climb to greater and greater scientific heights and so arrive at a true knowledge of God.

The basic religious question is not: "Is there a God, and can man know Him?" and true knowledge of God is not obtained by arguing about the pros and the cons of His existence. The basic religious question is: "Did God reveal himself?" and if He did the first question is answered in the affirmative. The answer to the second question does not come by weighing the pros and the cons of revelation in general and of the Biblical revelation in particular, but follows from listening to the Christian message, such that hearing becomes believing, trusting and obeying. That this happens does not lie within the power of those who bring the message but within the power of the Holy Spirit.

2. The relation between science, philosophy and theology in history[1-2].

In medieval times theology, philosophy and science formed a unity. This is best seen from the work of St. Thomas Aquinas. In St. Thomas' theological system human life is seen as a two-story structure. On the ground floor is the *natural life* known by reason and leading to a *natural knowledge* of God. On the top floor is the *supernatural life* governed by revelation and grace. Consequently, St. Thomas' theological system is also a two-story structure: Natural theology, known by reason, occupies the ground floor whereas the top floor contains the *supernatural theology* known by revelation. There is no doubt that the ground floor merely served as a base on which the top floor could be erected, but that it did not determine what went on on that floor. It opened, however, the connection to science and to Aristotelian philosophy.

The reformation made the break between philosophy and theology. This is especially clear in Luther's thinking. The rediscovered "justification by faith through grace" did not fit into St. Thomas' system at all and for that reason this system was dropped. But the Protestant theologians of the 16th and 17th century did not fully follow in the footsteps of the reformers. In their effort to build Protestant theology into a huge closed system of thinking, they had to revert to a closer relationship between philosophy and theology. A greater emphasis was put on natural theology and on human reason. As a consequence, philosophy gradually started to dominate theology, as is clear in the case of Leibniz and his followers. In the meanwhile, philosophy had moved away from the Aristotelian system.

The development of the natural sciences started with a break between science and philosophy. Formerly a scientific question was decided by quoting an earlier authority, in particular Aristotle. Gradually it became common practice to decide a question by experimentation followed by a theoretical discussion. This did not go without a struggle, as is seen, for example, from Galilei's life history.

The scientists of the 16th and 17th century were generally well versed in the Bible, and as such it was not so surprising that the Bible served as a framework for the upcoming sciences. Many names in geology (e.g. diluvium), biology (e.g. parthenogenesis) and anthropology (e.g. Semitic, Hamitic and Japhetic peoples and languages) still testify to this. This was dangerous theologically, since the Bible was not meant as such a framework. It was also dangerous scientifically, for the rapid developments in science made this framework less and less suited for it, since it threatened to strangle its growth.

One further example will be given. When systematic biology developed in the 18th century, it was more or less natural to suppose that the biological terms "species" or "genus" referred to the word "kind" in Genesis 1. As a consequence, the idea of "special creation" was introduced into biology as a *biological process*. This was dangerous theologically, for the Christian concept of Creation is not a biological concept, even where it refers to biological systems. Having thus downgraded this concept of Creation, it was unavoidable that any rival "biological explanation" of the origin of species, such as the theory of evolution, would be seen as a direct attack upon Christianity. Part of this conflict would have been avoided if it had been borne in mind that there is a radical difference between "Creation" and any biological process.

Sooner or later the sciences had to break out of this framework. Before this happened, however, an attempt was made to use the natural sciences as a support for theology. We saw in the third chapter how this attempt failed and why it had to fail. When science gradually broke out of the Biblical framework, this often meant a break with Biblical Christianity for the individual scientists. And that is not so surprising, for it was generally admitted that science was a necessary support for Christian theology. Consequently, if this support gave way, there was nothing left. What was often not understood, was that the whole idea was wrong. The Christian message and its systematic presentation, theology, are independent of science and thus cannot be supported by it or hampered by it.

This does not mean that there were no theologians, ministers and laymen left that did not try to maintain the basic content of the Christian message. It is to the credit of the conservative elements in the various churches that they aimed at maintaining it and that they actually did. However, they often did not sufficiently discriminate between the message as such and the theological framework of the 16th-17th century. This framework incorporated earlier scientific and philosophical thinking that had long since been discarded. Maintaining this framework caused intellectual difficulties for those inside the church and confusion and misunderstanding for those outside the church.

It is to the credit of the liberal elements in the various churches that they realized that this framework, belonging to the distant past, should be discarded. Unfortunately, their understanding of the Christian message was not deep enough to prevent that vital elements of the Christian message were discarded with it. In some cases that which remained could hardly be called Christian. Such a course of events is not surprising if human reason becomes the sole criterion of truth. It merely demonstrates what the Apostle Saint Paul said to the Galatian Christians: ". . . the Gospel which was preached of me was not after man."

It is against this background that the work of the Swiss theologian Karl Barth must be placed[1]. In it the source of theology and the Christian freedom with which a theologian can go about its task was rediscovered, and St. Paul's Epistle to the Romans played an important part in this rediscovery. His "Kirchliche Dogmatik" is a large-scale attempt to carry out a two-fold program of reformulating in modern form much what was said by earlier theologians and of removing discrepancies in earlier treatments by a renewed listening to what the Bible has to say. For the latter reason Barth's "Kirchliche Dogmatik" contains many detailed exegetic studies of those parts of the

Old and the New Testament that are of interest for the individual problems under study.

Theology is not something that can be put into its final form by a great theologian to be faithfully reproduced from then on. That would only repeat the difficulties that have beset theology since the 16th and 17th century. It is not carried out in an ivory tower, but aims at giving a systematic presentation of the Christian message for the world of *today*. This is a continuing challenge for each generation.

3. Relation between theology and science today.

It has been the aim of this book to point out that there is little positive relation between theology and science at present. And that this is as it should be, since they have little in common. For usually they look at different problems, and even if they look at the same problem they look at it from a different point of view, as we saw already.

There are, however, negative benefits to be obtained from science. For example, all of us are strongly influenced by the scientific, philosophical and political ideas of our environment. Even a theologian who tries to present the Christian message as faithfully as he can, will mix some of these ideas with his presentation. As mentioned before, this may cause trouble later. These ideas are obvious to him, but to a later generation they are not obvious at all, and in some cases they even turn out to be pertinently wrong. Modern science can give the theologians the (negative) benefit of pointing out that such mixing occurred in earlier times and can make them better aware of the dangers involved. It may help them to discriminate between *what* is said and the *way* it is said.

It is more important to look for parallels in the development of the natural sciences and theology[1-4]. Physics gives a systematic account of natural phenomena and theology gives a systematic account of the Christian message. What they have in common is not the *content* of the two fields, but the method of approach and the *systematic account* that they are trying to give. This is responsible for the parallels that can be observed. We mentioned already the concept of complementarity in physics and theology. We now discuss a few more parallels.

One parallel is the common relation to philosophy. Philosophy is necessary if one wants to gain clear concepts and clear distinctions. It serves as a tool rather than that it governs as a master. Philosophy does not decide what is natural science and what is not. Neither does it decide which concepts should be used and which should not, since that is determined by the object under study. Philosophy is merely the indispensable help in ordering and organizing the existing data and theories. If something goes wrong in the natural sciences, it helps little to turn to philosophy, but it is necessary to turn to experiment to clarify the situation.

Neither does philosophy decide the content and the scope of Christian theology. That is decided by the Christian message. It does not prescribe the methods that should be used in theology, since that is determined by its object. Philosophy is merely the indispensable help in giving a systematic exposition of its content. It something goes wrong in theology, it helps little to turn to philosophy, but it is necessary to turn to the Christian message itself to clarify the solution.

It is an unhealthy situation if philosophy predominates over the natural sciences or theology. The great upsurge of the natural sciences occurred after the predominance of medieval philosophy had been broken. The newer developments in theology, in particular in the case of Barth, started as a movement away from philosophy that had predominated 19th century European theology.

This freedom gained by the natural sciences and by theology is also important for the philosopher. Prof. Barth told me that he had found that philosophers became much more interested in his work after he had moved away from philosophy and had devoted himself exclusively to the pursuit of theology itself. The same can be said for the natural sciences. This is understandable, for new concepts, methods and ideas in the natural sciences or in theology give the philosopher new material for his work.

The relation between experiment and theory in the natural sciences has its parallel in the relation between Biblical exegesis and dogmatics in theology. In theology there is an intricate interrelation between Biblical exegesis and dogmatics. Dogmatics without exegesis and exegesis without dogmatics are threatened with sterility. The interplay between the two is necessary for a healthy situation. As can be learned from the literature, there is not always a good understanding between the exegetes and the dogmatists, especially not in Europe. It is not a good sign when representatives from the two groups have difficulty in communicating with each other. Both groups depend on each other for guidance and stimulation. This situation is parallel to the one in the natural sciences discussed in Chapter 2.

There are also important differences which are caused by the difference in subject matter. Theology is an effort of the Christian Church and its work is done in service of the Church. For that reason the Swiss theologian, Karl Barth, has called his main work: "Kirchliche Dogmatik." The natural sciences, however, do not have a similar relationship.

Another important difference between the natural sciences and theology is the following. The natural sciences are rapidly expanding and points of view often change dramatically if an existing field develops or a new field opens up. A textbook that is ten years old is already old-fashioned and not quite up to date in many places. If it is thirty years old it is probably mostly obsolete and if it is fifty years old it is probably only important for those interested in the history of science*. Except for a few cases it is usually not worth-while to consult a paper that is more than five years old and there are very few requests for reprints of papers that are older than that.

The Christian message, however, has not changed for almost 2000 years, neither are revolutionary changes in the most important Christian dogmas anticipated. Important upheavals in theological thinking have come about by a *rediscovery* of its origin, as during the start of the Reformation and in the case of Karl Barth[1].

The rapid changes in the natural sciences make it highly undesirable to tie the natural sciences and theology together. That can only spell trouble later, because the theologians would have to fight a constant rear guard battle to keep their theological thinking in line with science. An additional reason why the two disciplines should not be tied together is that they have so little in common. Those who keep this in mind avoid many difficulties.

It would be sad if the philosopher, the natural scientist and the theologian fully agreed on all occasions, for that would mean that they could not learn any more from each other. It would be equally sad if the three groups differed so strongly

---

*This does not mean that science in its present version is unreliable. Theologians who hope that future science will agree better with their ideas than present science are probably in for a disappointment.

that they could not even communicate with each other. What is needed is an openness to the others' problems, method of approach and point of view. I am pleased to admit that my contact with theologians has broadened my view and has thus indirectly helped me in my work.

4. Apologetics. The problem of communication.

Science is often used in attacks against Christianity as well as in its defense. Using it in an attack against Christianity indicates that one has not understood what the relation between science and the Christian message is. Using it in the defense of Christianity, as is often done in apologetic efforts, may suffer from the same defect.

Apology means defense. Defending Christianity means telling what it *is* and what it stands for. It is the weak point of many apologetic attempts that this elementary fact is not sufficiently appreciated. Instead, one attempts to find all sorts of secondary arguments that at best make Christianity plausible but that usually carry little convincing power. Many of these efforts are *attempts to defend something that does not need defense with means that cannot defend it.*

Though Christianity as such does not need defense it may be necessary to counteract an attack on Christianity by means of scientific arguments for three reasons. In the first place, it is important to demonstrate why the scientific objection does not hold. In the second place, the use of science against Christianity is a misuse of science and should be recognized as such. In the third place, it indicates a misunderstanding that should be removed. This is best done on an incidental basis.

In cases where a public attack has been made, a public rectification may be necessary and in that case it is important not to use unconvincing arguments. On a personal level, however, the situation is quite different. Here one *should not under-estimate the power of unconvincing arguments*. Although these arguments may not have the power to convince, they may have the power to eliminate mental roadblocks in the understanding of certain problems. This is a general experience of everyone who has taught school or lectured at universities*. It is difficult, however, to write a book of citations of unconvincing arguments.

We enter here into the problem of communicating the Christian faith to others. What may be unconvincing generally and sometimes even have a rather doubtful theological basis may be quite useful in approaching outsiders in individual cases: *For approaching others means meeting them on their own territory*. The Apostle Paul gives good examples of it in his letters and in his preaching, especially in his famous sermon in Athens (Acts 17:22-31):

1—St. Paul met many people that thought in allegoric terms and as a consequence he used allegoric interpretations of the Old Testament quite freely. At present such an allegoric approach is frowned upon in many circles and it would not be very useful.

2—In his sermon in Athens he referred to the worship of the unknown God, not because he approved of this worship, but because it gave him the analogy that the God whom he preached was indeed unknown to the Athenians.

3—In the same sermon he took up their belief in Providence, not because he necessarily agreed with it in detail, but because it gave him another analogy: The God whom Paul preached is a God who indeed provides.

---

*A student once asked me whether there was d-c sound. I answered him: "D-c sound is a draft." This was not an adequate answer to the question but it was at least effective in clarifying the situation.

4—Paul also referred to the Greek poets who had claimed: "For we are also the offspring of God." Theologically, Paul might have had something to say against such a claim, but in the practical situation that was not at issue. What was important was that what Paul preached would indeed make them children of God by faith.

5. World views[1].

The Christian message has ethical implications. One can distinguish here between the "facts" and the "charge."* The facts refer to Christ's coming into the world, His life, His death, His resurrection and the salvation that He has won. The "charge" refers to the implications that all this has for the Christian life. That is clear in St. Paul's epistle to the Romans: The first eleven chapters refer to the "facts" and the last chapters contain the "charge." A similar relation holds in other religions: there is a "story" (the facts) and there are ethical implications (the charge).

The same is not true in the natural sciences. There are facts all right, even an overwhelming number of them, but there are no ethical implications. The criteria of true or false in the natural sciences are independent of whether the scientist is a Christian or an atheist, a drinker or a teetotaler, married or unmarried, etc. Not that these things are unimportant; on the contrary, they are very important. However, they have nothing to do with the validity or invalidity of experimental data or theories in the natural sciences.

The opposite is also true. Studying the expanding universe, atomic nuclei, defects in crystalline solids or the genetics of the banana fly, will never lead to the command: "Thou shalt love thy neighbor as thyself." The reason is that science refers only

*I owe this approach to Prof. Holmer.

to *part* of human existence. If a scientist comes home to his wife and children, he enters into a realm completely different from the one in which his daily task is performed. Science gives facts but has no ethical implications. Religion does, since it aims at the *totality* of human existence.

This does not mean, of course, that scientific facts have no bearing on human decisions. Before it can be decided whether atomic bombs are good or evil, one has to know what they are and what they can do. There are many examples of similar situations. The scientific facts thus *enter into* the decision but do not fully determine it. Good and evil are ethical concepts, not concepts taken from the natural sciences.

People need some basis for their actions. If this basis is not provided by religion, they will develop a *world view*. A world view is a set of rules, concepts and relationships that can command and determine human actions and human lives. Such a world view has in common with religion that it has a *story* (the facts) and that it has a *charge* (the ethical implications). It is not necessarily a religion, but it is usually better to call it a pseudo-religion. Communism is a good example of it.

For this reason a so-called "scientific world view" is a contradiction in itself. How can something that has no ethical implications become the basis of ethical decisions? Only if the basis upon which the natural sciences operate is completely forgotten. On the other hand, it cannot be denied that most scientists are motivated in their work by some form of world view. What they achieve, however, in the scientific field of their choosing is not achieved *because* of their world view but often *despite* of it.

In a similar sense, a "Christian world view" is somewhat of a contradiction within itself. It makes out of the Christian message something that it is *not,* at least *not primarily.* The

Christian message is not primarily a set of rules, concepts and relationships that in and by themselves command human action and human life. Its primary aim is to establish a relation between man and God through faith in Christ and it is *that* relation that determines the Christian life. Changing the Christian message into a set of "Christian principles" is not uncommon and perhaps not always avoidable. It is one of the tasks of the theologians to keep the distinction between the two alive.

Theology and science have in common that they do not develop world views. Their attitude toward world views is different, however. Since world views do not determine what is true or false in the natural sciences, the natural scientist can ignore them. The theologian, however, must deal with them.

The following quotation indicates how, in Prof. Karl Barth's opinion, a Christian theology of creation should deal with world views (Kirchliche Dogmatik, Vol. III.1, pg. 393-394)[1]:

1) Sie kann nicht selbst Weltanschauung werden.

2) Sie kann sich auf keine Weltanschauung stützen.

3) Sie kann sich ihrerseits für keine Weltanschauung garantieren.

4) Sie kann ihre Aufgabe nicht darin sehen, sich partiell zustimmend zu ihnen und partiell ablehnend gegen sie zu stellen. Sie widerspricht ihnen einerseits gar nicht . . . Sie widerspricht ihnen aber anderseits grundsätzlich . . .

5) Sie führt das Gespräch mit den Weltanschauungen in der Weise, dass sie ihre eigene Erkenntnis . . . gegen jene stellt.

6) Sie geht unterdessen als Teil der Christlichen Dogmatik der eigenen Aufgabe nach.

Dass sind die Gründe weshalb Problemstellungen wie 'Naturalistische und religiöse Weltansicht' in dieser Darstellung der Christlichen Lehre von der Schöpfung nicht vorkommen kann.*

6. Scientists and the Christian message.

It is sometimes stated that modern developments in the natural sciences, especially in physics, should make the scientist more open to the Christian message (Heim)[5] and even that science is on its way to religion (Bavinck)[6]. It is difficult to prove such a statement and it is probably an exaggeration. For the removal of a few alleged misunderstandings, that were obstacles more in imagination than in fact, does not turn scientists into believers. The author knows several renowned scientists that are sincere Christians. He knows even more that would classify themselves as agnostics. That is nothing new, for the Apostle Paul had already a similar experience with the philosophers of his day.

The scientific attitude may indeed be a real obstacle for the Christian faith for the following reasons:

1—The habit of investigation, experimentation, observation and deduction may foster an attitude where the scientist feels himself the master who decides about truth and falsehood. The Christian message demands an altogether different attitude, however. Here, man is not the proud master, but the humble receiver of God's love and grace.

2—A scientist must be open to new possibilities, for what

---

*1) It cannot become a world view itself.
2) It cannot lean on any world view.
3) It cannot for its part give a guarantee for any world view.
4) It cannot see its task in taking a partially approving and partially disapproving attitude toward them. It does not contradict them at all on the one hand . . . It contradicts them fundamentally on the other hand . . .
5) It carries out the discussion with the world views in such a manner that it puts its own insight against theirs.
6) In the meanwhile it carries out its own task as part of the Christian dogmatics.
These are the reasons why problems like 'Naturalistic and religious world view' cannot occur in this presentation of the Christian Doctrine of creation.

is accepted today may have to be discarded tomorrow. With the Christian faith, however, the situation is different. It means not only starting to put one's trust in Christ but also remaining faithful to Him. For that reason faith is often compared to marriage in the Bible.

3—Sitting on the fence may be a good scientific attitude. The Christian message, however, calls people to the *decision* for Christ.

Becoming a Christian means that a scientist must turn from his familiar way of thinking to putting his faith in Christ. In other words he needs *conversion,* not only in this respect, but in other respects too. The obstacles for the Christian message may be different in his case; his situation in general is comparable to that of other people.

There are other obstacles. In the first place, it may happen that the religious training of a scientist has not gone beyond Sunday school, if he ever got that far, whereas he has a Ph.D. in his field of specialization. Such a condition is bound to raise conflicts and it is quite understandable that this conflict is resolved by turning away from religion. For that reason it is important that the religious training of a student continues during his university years. This training must recognize the particular situation in which the student finds himself, and it must be given in a manner that meets this situation. For example, it makes little sense to tell science majors that the world is only 6,000 years old. They know better. But it makes very good sense to discuss with them what the first chapters of Genesis try to tell, and why they tell it in the way they do.

There are many misunderstandings about the Christian message. An an example, I refer to the last chapter of Hoyle's book "The Nature of the Universe" entitled: "A Personal View." In most cases the misunderstandings are honest ones and we as Christians are partly responsible for it. It should be our concern not to stand in the way between others and God and prevent them to see what the Christian message actually is.

7. Our Christian task as scientists.

In my opinion the task of a scientist who is a Christian is not different from that of a non-Christian. Since there are different points of view in this matter, it is worth-while to discuss the problem in more detail.

Science is often used to build a "scientific world view." To counteract this, several Christians feel it as their Christian task to develop a *Christian philosophy of science.* I think that this would be the wrong solution to the problem. The Christian is not gifted with any special scientific or philosophical insight that the non-Christian does not have. It is not his task to build a system all of his own, but to keep the scientific discussion *open.*

Problems like the certainty of our scientific knowledge and the possible unification of various fields of knowledge are truly scientific problems and not primarily philosophical ones, though philosophers will be rightly interested in the results. Drawing conclusions about the *physical* presuppositions of the natural sciences is also a genuinely scientific task. Drawing conclusions about the *philosophical* consequences of these presuppositions, however, is not a scientific task but a philosophical one. It would be arrogant to think that it is a higher form of life than merely advancing the frontiers of human knowledge. Neither is it a scientific task to use the natural sciences for drawing conclusions about world views or to investigate the rapid changes in world view resulting from the developments in the sciences. It would again be arrogant to presume that it is a higher form of life than just establishing new facts and new theories. Since they are nonscientific tasks, it makes little sense to compete with them by developing a Christian philosophy of science or a Christian world view compatible with science.

One cannot develop a world view and stay within the borders of science. If one does so, it implies stepping outside of those borders. Everybody is free to do so, of course, as long as he does not claim that he is pursuing a scientific task. Sticking to the scientific task means *abstaining* from developing scientific world views. History shows that this is difficult. Man seems to have a natural tendency to develop world views and many scientists have a tendency to develop *scientific* world views. That, however, *is not a consequence of science but is a human habit.*

The ones who ought to be able to overcome this tendency are the Christians. For them the firm foundation of their lives does not lie in science but in Jesus Christ. They are set free to pursue their field of science in a truly worldly manner, for the certainty of their lives lies elsewhere. A non-Christian *should be* equally worldly in his pursuit of science, but he often *is not.* Especially in the past it was often tried to give science a pseudo-religious color by developing a scientific world view. Developing a Christian philosophy of science would mean a direct competition with a wrong tendency. Not to deny our Christian freedom is therefore our Christian task as scientists.

We have another task that is closely associated with it. Bright and learned people make complicated errors in thinking that are difficult to unravel. The natural sciences have the advantage over other sciences that many of the errors can be checked by experiment and thus be easily eliminated. Errors that are not open to experimental test have a longer life. This is especially true for erroneous applications of the natural sciences to fields such as philosophy or theology. It is our task to unravel and eliminate these errors.

There is often a tendency to make the natural sciences, or some of the other sciences for that matter, into a closed system of thinking. In such a system, usually only a limited part of human inquiry finds a place, whereas the remaining part is excluded. It is our task to keep the natural sciences open and not to block the path to other fields of human experience.

Being a Christian does not make a man a better scientist; to claim so would be arrogant and conceited. He has, however, as a privilege, that he can do his scientific work under Christian freedom, without having to fear that the results of his work might upset the foundation of his life. For those who are motivated in their scientific work by their desire to develop a scientific world view, this is not the case.

REFERENCES:

[1]Karl Barth, *Kirchliche Dogmatik*, Evangelischer Verlag, Zollikon-Zürich.

[2]Karl Barth, *Die Protestantische Theologie im 19. Jahrhundert*, Evangelischer Verlag, Zollikon-Zürich.

[3]G. Henneman, *Philosophie, Religion, Moderne Naturwissenschaft*, l.c.

[4]H. H. Schrey, *Weltbild und Glaube im 20 Jahrhundert*, l.c.

[5]Karl Heim, *Die Wandlung im naturwissenschaftlichen Weltbild-Die moderne Naturwissenschaft vor der Gottesfrage*, Hamburg, 1951.

[6]Bernard Bavink, *Das Weltbild der heutigen Naturwissenschaften und seine Beziehungen zu Philosophie und Religion, Iserlohn*, 1947.

Name Index

Index